THE PHYSIOLOGY OF EMOTIONS

the
Physiology of Emotions

Report of the Third Annual Symposium of the Kaiser
Foundation Hospitals in Northern California, San Francisco

ALEXANDER SIMON, M.D., Editor
Professor and Chairman, Department of Psychiatry
University of California School of Medicine
Medical Director, Langley Porter Institute
San Francisco

CHARLES C. HERBERT, M.D., Associate Editor
Chief of Medicine and Director of Medical Education
Kaiser Foundation Hospital
San Francisco

RUTH STRAUS, Assistant Editor
Department of Publication
Kaiser Foundation Hospitals
Oakland, California

With a Preface by
CLIFFORD H. KEENE, M.D.
Vice President
The Kaiser Foundation
Oakland, California

CHARLES C THOMAS • PUBLISHER
Springfield • Illinois • U.S.A.

CHARLES C THOMAS • PUBLISHER
Bannerstone House
301-327 East Lawrence Avenue, Springfield, Illinois, U.S.A.

Library of Congress Catalog Card Number: 60-12675

With THOMAS BOOKS *careful attention is given to all details of manufacturing and design. It is the Publisher's desire to present books that are satisfactory as to their physical qualities and artistic possibilities and appropriate for their particular use.* THOMAS BOOKS *will be true to those laws of quality that assure a good name and good will.*

Printed in the United States of America

PARTICIPANTS AND DISCUSSANTS

ROY R. GRINKER, M.D.

Director, Institute for Psychosomatic
and Psychiatric Research and Training; Chairman
Division of Neuropsychiatry; Michael Reese Hospital, Chicago, Illinois

H. W. MAGOUN, Ph.D.

Professor of Anatomy, School of Medicine
University of California at Los Angeles
Veterans Administration Hospital
Long Beach, California

HUDSON HOAGLAND, Ph.D., Sc.D.

Executive Director
Worcester Foundation for Experimental Biology
Shrewsbury, Massachusetts

WILLIAM F. GANONG, M.D.

Assistant Professor of Physiology
University of California Medical Center
San Francisco, California

PETER FORSHAM, M.D.

Professor of Medicine and Pediatrics
Director Metabolic Unit for Research in Arthritis and Allied Diseases
University of California
San Francisco, California

SEYMOUR S. KETY, M.D.

Chief, Laboratory of Clinical Science
National Institute of Mental Health
National Institutes of Health, Public Health Service
U. S. Department of Health, Education, and Welfare
Bethesda, Maryland

ALAN GOLDFIEN, M.D.

Assistant Professor of Medicine (Obstetrics and Gynecology)
Research Associate in Physiology
University of California
San Francisco, California

JOEL ELKES, M.D.

Chief, Clinical Neuropharmacology Research Center
National Institute of Mental Health
National Institutes of Health, U. S. Public Health Service
Director of Research, Saint Elizabeths Hospital
U. S. Department of Health, Education, and Welfare
Clinical Professor of Psychiatry, George Washington University
Washington, D. C.

R. M. FEATHERSTONE, Ph.D.

Professor and Chairman
Department of Pharmacology and Experimental Therapeutics
University of California
San Francisco, California

FRANK A. BEACH, Ph.D.

Professor of Psychology
University of California
Berkeley, California

RALPH W. GERARD, M.D., Ph.D.

Director of Laboratories
Mental Health Research Institute
University of Michigan
Ann Arbor, Michigan

KARL H. PRIBRAM, M.D.

Associate Professor of Psychiatry and Psychology
Department of Psychiatry
Stanford University School of Medicine
Palo Alto, California

DAVID McK. RIOCH, M.D.

Director, Division of Neuropsychiatry
Walter Reed Army Institute of Research
Walter Reed Army Medical Center
Washington, D. C.

CHARLES C. HERBERT, M.D.

Chief of Medicine and Director of Medical Education
Kaiser Foundation Hospital
San Francisco, California

MAURICE S. GOLDSTEIN, M.D.

Director, Department of Metabolic and Endocrine Research
Michael Reese Hospital
Chicago, Illinois

EDWIN A. WEINSTEIN, M.D.

Clinical Director, Bureau of Mental Health
St. Thomas, Virgin Islands
Consultant, Division of Neuropsychiatry
Walter Reed Army Institute of Research
Walter Reed Army Medical Center
Washington, D. C.

PREFACE

Man has always examined his emotions, translating them into the equivalents of whatever sciences might be fashionable. The humors of the body, the bumps on the skull, and the position of the stars have been held in serious regard by our not too distant predecessors who have attended this problem. The translation of emotions into the physiologic complexities of present day chemistry, physics, and anatomy still leaves a remnant which is elusive and mysterious.

These observations of eminent teachers and researchers upon this provocative subject were made at the Third Annual Symposium sponsored by the Kaiser Medical Care entities held in San Francisco on October 9 and 10, 1959. These annual meetings are projected for the edification of all who are interested in the improvement of man's physical and mental wellbeing, and in broadening the frontiers of knowledge, and are intended to enhance the professional climate of our community.

To the physicians of The Permanente Medical Group we express thanks for organizing and executing the details of the meeting. Special mention in this regard must be made of the efforts of Dr. Martin A. Shearn, and Dr. Charles C. Herbert.

CLIFFORD H. KEENE, M.D.
Vice President
The Kaiser Foundation

Oakland, California

CONTENTS

THE PHYSIOLOGY OF EMOTIONS

I

THE PHYSIOLOGY OF EMOTIONS

ROY R. GRINKER, M.D.

I

THE physiology of emotions is truly of great importance for psychiatry and all of medicine as a precursor to the understanding of emotions' pathogenic roles. Anxiety is the most significant emotion and to some degree accompanies all others. It is not only a signaler of danger and leads to defensive and restrictive mechanisms, but is also a symptom of disturbance and an end product of a breakdown of integration. At the point of disintegration many psychic and somatic functions are profoundly disorganized, at which time they may become symptomatic of some diseases.

Almost twenty-five years ago Dunbar wrote a book entitled *Emotions and Bodily Changes* and within five years founded the now well known periodical *Psychosomatic Medicine*. Today the appearance of these two publications may be considered as milestones in a chain of events which have had a tremendous impact on psychiatry and medicine. In 1939 the notion of a psychosomatic approach to all illness and particularly to a few so-called degenerative diseases seemed revolutionary. At least it was considered by contemporary physicians to be something new, but this was a false notion maintained by a process of forgetting or never knowing the history of medicine. Parenthetically, I might say that current medical scholars often ignore the historical approach and make little reference to past efforts and contributions.

As a matter of fact, the word *psychosomatic* had been used in the last century, and certainly what it designated was only a recapitulation of the mind-body problem which men had thought and written about since antiquity. Indeed, all classical philosophers

3

had devoted considerable effort, without much available scientific evidence, to attempting to resolve the dualistic concept of mind and body, which seems to be one of our many "common sense" fallacies. Only a few outstanding individuals had been able to consider that thinking and feeling were basically not different from motion and sensation. But even the earliest medicine men whose writings have been preserved had gathered empirical evidence that mind and body, although considered to be separate entities, in some way affected each other. For example, black bile produced melancholia, and disturbances in the cerebral vapors caused physical weakness.

In modern times the concept that the physical attributes of man constitute processes apart, and entirely different, from his cognitive and emotional functions is no longer seriously maintained. Rather early in this century, phrases such as the "organism as a whole" or the "total person," and in recent times the words "psychosomatic" and "comprehensive medicine" have epitomized what might be called a global or a unitary concept. Although the broad sweep of this concept was startling at first, it has now lost its charm because technical operations have been inadequate for its applications to the study of health and disease.

The history of medicine has demonstrated that the study and understanding of any well integrated and functioning whole system is extremely difficult. Certainly clinical research has concentrated on the use of natural and contrived experiments in which the whole is at least partially fragmented. The study of pathophysiology has been the approach by which healthy functioning in man could be better understood. In fact, for an understanding of his total role behavior within a social group, man can be viewed operationally only as a psychosomatic unity. To describe, analyze, and understand the disorders of man in disease, by which one may hope to reach a better understanding of his functions in health, a position must be taken which facilitates a view of the functional relationships of his component parts.

When these parts are exposed for study after disintegrations which we call diseases, they have usually been analyzed on the basis of the traditional medical model under the domination of the concept of specificity. Medicine had considered that for every disease syndrome there should be a specific etiological microbe, virus, chemical deficiency, or metabolic derangement. The modern approach has replaced these causes by specific complexes of emotional turbulence precipitated by appropriate external stimuli.

The specificity point of view has not only perpetuated the notion of a single most effective causal factor but has also facilitated the creation of stereotypes. The current psychosomatic model over-emphasizes psychogenesis and asserts that particular kinds of emotional problems are always related to the cause of specific diseases. Thus, peptic ulcer is derived from repressed and unacceptable passive and dependent yearnings; whereas essential hypertension is considered to be the result of repressed hostility. Originally, essential psychological causal factors were correlated with so-called "personality profiles" which presumed to differentiate people who were susceptible to various diseases. But these profiles were based on impractical "split-hair" differences obtained by clinical impressions. At deeper unconscious levels, tapped by psychoanalytic investigations, the specific complexes presumably related to individual diseases were concatenations of dependency, frustration, and hostility, all of which are monotonous universals in human nature.

Over the years enthusiasm for first the holistic approach and then the specificity concepts abated considerably. The former, although conceptually sound, is still incapable of analysis; the latter is a simplified and analyzable concept which stirred enthusiastic interest in the field and, much later, disappointment from frustration. Progress was slowed for a long time because we did not know enough about the physiology of emotions nor did we have methods adequate for learning more.

II

What do we really know about mind-body relationships as they are involved in health and disease? Freud spoke of the "mysterious leap from psyche to soma" when he considered hysterical conversion symptoms which seemed to involve only innervations from the somatic nervous system. In the meantime the so-called "specific psychosomatic disturbances," which include hypertension, peptic ulcer, ulcerative colitis, rheumatoid arthritis, thyrotoxicosis, migraine, asthma, hay fever, etc., are supposedly mediated through mechanisms that involve only autonomic innervations.

Lately Freud's followers have been attempting to reinterpret his words, but actually the notion that specific diseases are expressions of disturbed innervations of *parts* of the nervous system has been unequivocally proved to be erroneous. In every disease of man both the somatic and autonomic nervous system as well as other processes are involved.

Countless clinical observations have enabled us to make some fairly sound generalizations. What we do know is that at some time and through neural or humoral mechanisms, among diseases, emotional disturbance appears, never as a single cause in the chain of events, but either as one of the causes or effects, as a precipitant of the onset, or a prolongator of the course, and as a factor in the resulting remission, response to treatment, or chronicity.

If we were to revert to the language of dualism, we would say that we know little about the functional relationships between mentation and body and the mechanisms by which these are achieved. However, if we adhere to the unitary concept of mentation and body, what we mean is that we do not know to what degree and in what temporal sequences organismal disturbances are expressed by a variety of nervous innervations and corresponding behaviors.

Some physiologists believe that mentation can never be explained in terms of neural energy. Other distinguished psychologists have been hopeful that correlations between neural and mental activities in man would eventually reveal a complete identity of these two processes. Many psychophysiologists have been optimistic that the painful contradiction between mentation and body will be eventually solved. However, at the present time it is difficult to make specific statements which, if transposed from mentation to body or vice versa, do not show profound inconsistencies.

This is certainly true if one wishes to be literal and direct. But the attempt to identify neurological mechanisms and psychological functions and to make direct correlations between them has been both too rigorous and at the same time too abstract. Perhaps the problem should be attacked more operationally, and we should observe and describe man's behaviors from several frames of reference with a hope of an eventual synthesis and unitary abstraction.

III

Since any single view of man's behavior is only a spatially and temporally limited focus, it becomes necessary to define a total field and at the same time to identify its parts. Thus man may be considered as a total field whose processes in action may be termed behaviors, all of which are transactionally related directly or indirectly with each other. The parts of this field identified as foci of observation are unlimited in number depending on the questions raised and the techniques available for observing. They may range from the physico-chemical structure of his somatic cells to his ethical and moral behavior. There are, however, certain conventional foci such as the anatomy and physiology of organs and organ systems concerned with energy exchange, transformation and storage. In relation to other similar organisms, his fellow men, he is a motivated thinking and feeling individual behaving in a specified space-time dimension. Or we may view him in relation to various aspects of his physical and animated environment in motion and as a part of various sized social groups. Obviously we may extend the number of viewable foci indefinitely into larger or smaller systems, but man cannot be well understood without knowing the structure-functions of his parts and the extent of his surroundings. Any change in one aspect has a reverberating effect on every other.

In this effort to observe various functions of man, we view him from different frames of reference. In so doing we are looking at different identifiable aspects of a total system which require separate scientific disciplines (since each one is concerned with another view of man), utilize specific methods, and report their findings in their own specially developed vocabularies. It becomes necessary, in order to view the many parts and processes of man in nature that are affected by and that influence his surroundings, to utilize a multidisciplinary approach.

Granted that man is a unique animal in his capacity for symbolization and verbalization, yet many of his systems of organization are, if not identical, similar to those of other animals. Man's particular types of behavior have not developed *de novo*. Step by step systems with new forms of organization and differentiated laws and regulations have evolved. Fundamental to all of them, however, are certain basic patterns of all living systems which enable us to make analogies from one function or process to another. However, each evolved system has introduced extended and modified functions which, in addition to a certain commonality with those of other systems, require new concepts for an understanding of the system's orderly regulations.

Each system of organization may be viewed as being part of a larger whole system, *ad infinitum*. In the processes of disintegration the parts of each organization become released to again become wholes or revived, partially independent systems. For each part and for each whole certain basic principles of organization may be epitomized as follows: 1. There are processes which maintain the integration of the organization and which resist disintegration. 2. For each part or for each whole organization, no matter where it lies in time or space, there are specific intrinsic functions. 3. Finally, for each system there are functions which are observable only in its relationship to other systems.

The most important system concerned with integration and resistance against disintegration is the central nervous system, which influences all somatic organs and is influenced by them as in the reciprocal relationship between movement and sensation. Certainly no significant psychological process goes on without the participation of the central nervous system. In fact, no significant integration of part function or total behavior, or for that matter any functional process develops, proceeds, or is disintegrated without involving the central nervous system. Aside from some indigenous and idling activity and a steady tonic influence which constantly relates the inside with the outside of the organism, the central nervous system operates most significantly in the rapid excitations or inhibitions that are involved in starting or stopping an activity.

The central nervous system has at least three significant major outflows. The first is the voluntary nervous system, which innervates striated muscles and is also concerned with incoming impulses from the specialized sensory organs receiving stimuli from the outer environment. The second is the autonomic nervous system, which influences all glands and smooth muscles. The third is the endocrine system, whose central locus resides in the neuroendocrine areas at the base of the brain (perhaps even in higher centers) and is intimately connected with the pituitary body, through which reciprocal influences regulate the outlying glands of internal secretion. None of these systems is independent of influences from the actions of the external and internal environment, nor does any one of these systems function independently of the other. They are not only integrated to a large degree centrally but also overlap in their functions and in their reciprocal effects on each other peripherally. To such an extent does this occur that it is often difficult to determine the preponderance of the influence of one outflow on any one of the target organs.

IV

There is a fairly well proved ancient axiom in medicine that the component parts of the healthy organism are relatively silent and their functional activities do not lend themselves to analysis. On the other hand, when there is trouble within the organism of any sort, the subject experiences sensations and explicit or implicit alterations in physical or psychological behavior. If we wish to understand mind-body and its complicated participation in disease, we must necessarily turn to those conditions in which dynamic equilibrium is in some way disturbed. There are many experiments in nature associated with disturbances in equilibrium, and there are now procedures available for experimentally inducing them under controlled conditions of observation. If a disturbance appears in the mental processes or we produce such a disturbance artificially, we can then view what functional processes are or are not upset within the somatic organs and vice versa. With adequate quantitative methods, we should be able to demonstrate that disorders of function appear simultaneously in both the psychic and somatic

systems. Current methodological problems consist in (1) developing reliable quantitative scales for measuring psychic functions;
(2) designing experiments permitting simultaneity of observations;
and (3) developing statistical methods for handling the large
amount of accrued data.

If we wish to study the relationships between mental and
somatic functions, it becomes necessary to focus simultaneously
on the most significant variables in each system. It seems like a
simple matter to choose from empirical data one or another
variable which has demonstrated the most frequent change or has
shown the greatest excursion in the presence of strong emotion.
This happens to be the cardiovascular system, which is extremely
sensitive to respond with all emotions. But it is far distant from the
central nervous system, and it is also a responder to many peripheral circulatory substances. Since the central nervous system is
concerned intimately with both psychological and physiological
processes and their integration, finding significant indices of its
functions that can be measured in the intact human may enable us
to approach the elucidation of psychophysiological integration.

Unfortunately we are not certain which significant variables are
closest to central nervous system activity, and some that we have
thought to be significant, prove not to be so. For example, we
would not be too much concerned with the degree or speed of
dilatation of the pupil or skin resistance or peripheral vasomotor
changes in the presence of strong emotion; they are too far peripheral. We would be much more interested in tapping the electrical
activity of the hypothalamus, but unfortunately this is not easily
approachable in the intact animal and certainly not easily in man.
We would feel fortunate if we could elicit the physiological
processes involved in meaningful incoming stimuli that trigger off
psychophysiological responses, but can not get any closer than the
subject's reporting of his conscious, often unreliable, interpretation
of meaning. Likewise, up to now we have not been able to measure
the direct activity of the endocrine glands in intact man, but must
be content with indirect estimations of production, utilization, and
metabolism by measuring various circulating or excreted hormones. Furthermore, in the living human being the activity of the

various target organs such as heart, blood vessels, gastrointestinal tract, respiratory system, etc., do not give us a clear picture of the specific activities of one of the cerebral outflows, since both autonomic nervous system and circulating hormones have a profound effect on all visceral activities. From the psychological point of view we can only utilize reports from the subject and responses to special tests of uncertain value to observe changes in the cognitive functions of perception and decision-making and in the connotative functions of coordinated psychomotor activity.

Experimental methods applied to the study of the physiology of human emotions are restricted by many ethical considerations. The resulting makeshifts are often seriously disappointing and probably account for the wildly unscientific conclusions abounding in the literature. Two events disparate in time and rarely confirmed are presumed to be significantly related. Subjective symptoms are used to replace objective observations. From vague clinical data explanatory concepts are unabashedly reported with certainty.

Indeed the experimental method in this field is difficult. Only a limited block of time is possible, simultaneity of observations by several disciplines is only relative, and many tests can be performed only once. The vast variety of uncontrollable stimuli extraneous to the experimental condition is often discouraging. Yet with adequate "before," "during," and "after" observations and with quantitative methods for estimating types and degrees of emotional responses, many valuable data can be acquired.

I have spoken about the use of already developed diseases to further our understanding of psychophysiology. Although in such natural experiments there is a wide range of disordered functions that the patient can point out for study, they are not always symptomatic at the time when there is an emotional disturbance. Thus, if a particularly significant stimulus impinges on a human being, it may be hours or days before this meaningful impact registers either psychologically or physiologically. It is this long latent period before discernible effect that makes it so difficult to ascertain what are the essential precipitating factors. Therefore, in the presence of a particular physiological disturbance one can not always be sure that the current emotional state is significantly related to it.

In our studies of paratroopers undergoing the stress of training, we found that anxiety could be evinced rather rapidly and only a few days later would biochemical indices of endocrine disturbance be found. In other individuals the biochemical processes could be discovered much sooner than the subject reported any emotional disturbance. This out-of-phase timing of responses or relationship between them makes it most difficult to determine the series of events through time which are necessary for the disturbance within the psyche to become evidenced in the somatic and vice versa.

We also are unsure of the relationship between various somatic processes which ultimately lead to profound disturbances in function. Thus, for example, the timing of disturbances may be the result of the requirement that one system be activated before the other; or perhaps the toxic product of one system of degradation is necessary before another activity is mobilized; or it may be necessary that a certain substance be produced in order to serve as a donor for the manufacture of another chemical substance. For all these reasons we realize that the best we can do at present in determining the relationships between the psychic and somatic and between various part functions of each is to categorize patterns of quantitative and temporal gradients. But we must recognize that at present what we can observe or measure may be intervening variables and that the most significant factors may still be unknown.

Physicians concerned with human disturbances are particularly interested in the antecedent state of the organism before it responds to significant stimuli with a disturbance of equilibrium. Thus we are interested in particular types of resting or idling equilibrium and their latent deficiencies which are antecedent and predisposing to the development of illness. What predispositions are there in the idling equilibrium which, in the presence of the proper meaningful precipitating factor, will result in a disease?

We know that many people are prone to anxiety resulting from a variety of past psychological experiences. We know, too, that anxiety can be stirred up by the impending eruption of a wide variety of unresolved conflicts. Such proneness may have been expressed in action in previous life situations as evidenced by the anecdotal material in a detailed longitudinal life history. We can only conjecture that this predisposing factor or conditioning results from some special constitutional factors on which early environmental influences were important. In studying the relationship of emotions and bodily changes, we need not be concerned if such emotions are latent or so-called "unconscious." They are of significance for our understanding of the problem if they are conscious or reportable by verbal or nonverbal behavior.

We are, furthermore, not acquainted with the intimate number of possible stimuli in early life which may have produced a somatic conditioning that results in a predisposition of a particular organ or organ system to react in the presence of adequate stress. We are beginning to understand the special mother-child relationship not only as it conditions somatic behavior expressed by various kinds of motor activity, but we are also aware of the fact that the type and rate of differentiation of visceral activities and their range of activities are affected by particular mother-child relationships. We can at this time only postulate that such somatic conditioning seems to be a prerequisite for the selection of particular foci of organ vulnerability.

The precipitating factors important for the production of a disturbance either psychic or somatic or both apparently have some significant bearing upon the quantity and locus of the disturbance. Without question, the precipitating factor for emotions must have psychic meaning, and we may use the same expression and also say "somatic meaning" in the sense that a stimulus overstrains a predisposed organic system. However, at this time we can not predict, from the meaning to the subject of the precipitating factor, the nature of the predisposition, nor can we predict what actual disturbance of equilibrium will be the outcome.

Stresses that evoke psychophysiological responses can not be defined by what we think should disturb people, since they must be personally meaningful to the subject. Stress should be defined only as a response which indicates that the organism has in some way been affected, no matter how trivial the conditions may seem to an observer.

As in any functional process, we are concerned with understanding not only the temporal factors of the development of the disturbance, but also its curve of decline or re-equilibrium and the timing of the temporary and long-term adaptations. We know that in biological systems that have a large factor of safety, the capacity for adaptation is great. Also, many systems function in complementarity and take over the activities of a disturbed or damaged system. Furthermore, there are adequate means by which the system defends itself against significant psychological stimuli, often by ignoring them through denial, a defense which remains adequate for long periods and may prevent the impact of the environment from becoming obvious to either the subject or the observer.

Some disturbances result in long-lasting disequilibrium which ends in so-called "diseases." These, too, may often be dealt with adequately by compensating functions or by adaptation to deficit. However, there is up to now no proved simple relationship between emotional processes and a specific disease, not even if we should include the most important predisposing factors. Many somatic disturbances of one type or another may occur simultaneously or in succession, within the same patient. There are many final private pathways for stresses and stress responses.

From both studies of disease and experiments there is little information about the mechanisms by which *long-standing* emotional disturbances result in tissue changes. Neither chronic elevation nor decline of metabolic functions can be demonstrated, and prolonged chronic excessive nervous innervations of special organs are not observed. In fact, state hospital patients with chronic depressions, whose capacities to exist in the outside world without the support of a parental figure (although the person who has borne such a projection may be dead or rejecting) are practically nil, reveal a curious nonreactivity. They are aroused with difficulty to any degree of either psychic or somatic response by even the most vigorous psychic pressure. Rather than a psychosomatic disease, they seem to acquire a chronic state of non-reactivity and react only to interference with their adjustment.

Perhaps it may now be understood somewhat better that the so-called "psychosomatic disturbances" or "mind-body dysfunctions" require much more information for their elucidation, all the details of which are rarely available from clinical observations. On the other hand, experimental disturbances in humans can only be acute and short-lasting, and, although they may imitate what we think occurs in the chronic natural state, it is by no means certain that the results of these experimental processes are proto-types of mechanisms to be found in psychosomatic illnesses.

V

I should now like to discuss in some detail the problem of anxiety, which is the most important affect related to man's functions in health and disease. Anxiety is a feeling state which is so unendurable to man that it evokes defensive maneuvers which in themselves are symptomatic and their clusters or syndromes comprise the entire spectrum of psychiatric and psychosomatic disorders.

There are emotions other than anxiety; certainly anger and depression are powerful forces in the human economy, and many other combinations of feeling states may be defined. At the present level of our knowledge, the three emotions mentioned are easier to study because they are not only reportable by the subject but they also have measurable somatic concomitants and behavioral manifestations. In general they are associated with the same variety of physiological patterns. Curiously, even the patient with the withdrawn and isolated type of depression shows in the early stages a steroid and cardiovascular pattern similar to that of anxiety. Anger, if it is suppressed, is associated with more pronounced physiological changes.

In differentiating anxiety from fear, we often state that anxiety is an internal state of foreboding; whereas fear is a response to an actual danger to the organism. The presence or absence of real and external danger is, however, not an adequate criterion for differentiating fear from anxiety. Under certain conditions which seem to be associated with usual or minimal quantities of danger, the organism reacts overwhelmingly as though it were confronted with a life-and-death situation. Here anxiety exists even though there is a nucleus of cause of fear. Anxiety, then, is a reaction which signifies an internal meaningfulness to the person experiencing it — a meaningfulness which the subject tends to attribute to reality. We have been unable to detect biological differences between states of fear and the psychic states of anxiety. However, our methods may not be adequate or our foci of observations may not be appropriate to the elucidation of the biological differences between these two phenomena.

Anxiety is an ubiquitous emotion present in all of us at various times in life, perhaps only with greater intensity in some and/or during various periods of development. It is essentially a signal of danger that some unacceptable impulse might erupt into consciousness and lead to behavior or conflicts detrimental to the subject or forbidden by society.

An analogous signal in the somatic sphere occurring in the presence of meaningful psychic or somatic danger is the mobilization of adrenocorticotropic hormone from the pituitary body, which stimulates the excretion of 17-hydroxysteroid from the adrenal cortex. Mobilization of this pituitary hormone, now commonly called an "alarm reaction," is quantitatively similar whether the danger is traumatization of the body by a surgical procedure, injury, cold, or a disturbing emotion.

A third analogous signal is derived from the social environment in the form of rumors, including implicit communications that are meaningful and impinge on a prepared receptivity. The stimulus is contained in the content, form, timing, or quantity of communication, expressed either verbally or nonverbally, warning that the subject is threatened by the expectation of an excessive degree of "higher-than-threshold" conformity or what in current American language is euphemistically called "togetherness." At the other extreme the content of the communication may be isolation from the group, either actual or threatened, through abandonment by other persons or by their rejection threatened by blocking or distorting, painful or excessive quantity of messages, or by actual physical isolation experimentally in a tank, immersed in water, or in a seclusion chamber. Because individuals can exist only in relation to other individuals and that not continually and constantly, either excessive participation in a group or isolation from it results in a diminution or loss of identity during which ego boundaries become loosened and primitive primary processes of thinking and feeling are liberated. In their most extreme forms these experimentally evoked disturbances have resulted in overt psychotic behavior, delusions, and hallucinations.

It has been demonstrated that anxiety, mobilization of the pituitary-adrenal system, and significant threatening rumors, although each primarily disturbs a different system of organization, are all associated with the same basic psychosomatic patterns. In order to exemplify these fundamental patterns, I shall discuss only anxiety.

Anxiety may be evoked by threatening internal somatic processes, by psychological stimuli meaningful to a particular subject, or by difficulties in social adjustment. Anxiety is an indescribable foreboding or dread of personal doom and has no proper external reference except as emergency defense in which people attempt to ascribe this feeling to some external situation which they then avoid. Anxiety probably has an evolution in the sense that it develops out of the fear responses of lower animals, but takes its special form because man's use of symbols enables him to understand the difference between I and not-I, and because he is able to project himself into the future and to understand the implicit meaning or consequence of his thoughts and acts.

Anxiety has an ontogenesis in that it develops in each human being in different forms and to different degrees. Its physical concomitants are all present at birth even though the feeling state is then not yet experienced or reportable. It is experienced and expressed nonverbally, however, by the child at about the eighth month when it becomes aware of the difference between itself and its mother and understands the meaning of separation from her. No child or adult is free from anxiety. As a matter of fact, optimum quantities are facilitative for the development of ego boundary processes and hence self-identity. Likewise, in optimum quantities it is facilitative for learning and adaptation, and intensifies efficiency of appropriately handled skilled action. It has recently been demonstrated experimentally that in infantile animals learning may be hastened and simultaneously an earlier appearance of the pituitary adrenal secretions may occur by minimal handling and separation from the mother.

Anxiety has been shown to preserve cortical dominance under stress and to protect against desynchronization in experimentally induced convulsions by elevating the threshold to these generalized forms of behavior. Furthermore, it is antagonistic to the desynchronization of cortical activities in sleep and, as is well known, the greater the anxiety, the higher the threshold for sleep.

It is not my purpose to discuss the facilitative properties of anxiety but, to the contrary, its destructive effects. Anxiety in optimum quantities intensifies efficiency, but at a certain peak of intensity it decreases facilitation and increases destructive effects. Somewhere in this curvilinear process defenses are stimulated which may take any of several forms. One is an attempt to deny the presence of the anxiety-producing stimulus; another to deny and defend against the presence of anxiety; and the third a defense against the effects of anxiety. Nevertheless, eventually the effects on the boundary or ego-functions of the personality which control the differentiation of self and not-self become extreme to the point where the whole world seems dangerous and panic ensues. The effects on cognitive functions, on behavior, and on the body are often severe. A large number of failures in psychological functions also result, and eventually behavior becomes disturbed to the point of fugue-like panic states. At some time in this curve of effects profound physiological disturbances develop.

Psychiatric and psychosomatic patterns of disturbance which are designated by special names represent patterns of defense against anxiety or its effects. Phobic avoidance, compulsive rituals, schizoid withdrawal, and other defenses represent attempts to avoid some aspect of the anxiety syndrome. This is clearly evidenced by the fact that, when any psychiatric or psychosomatic process is manipulated by treatment, as, for example, medication, surgical excision, or psychotherapy, anxiety is usually liberated. It matters not whether this procedure is psychotherapy, hypnosis, narcosynthesis, or various forms of somatotherapy. The reduction or removal of defenses is associated with the recrudescence of anxiety which often further disturbs therapy if it is permitted to become intense. It is, therefore, one of the skills of therapeutic maneuvers in psychiatric techniques to dose the quantity of anxiety in order to produce sufficient tension for relearning but not sufficient anxiety for flight.

The particular kind of flight of greatest interest to an understanding of the physiology of emotions is regression — that is, the giving up of the delicately balanced differentiations of functions characteristic of maturity and achieved through the slow ontogenesis of man in his developmental period. From an undifferentiated psychosomatic organism, part functions begin to differentiate and become specialized, although still well integrated in the total organismic functions. In the presence of anxiety there is a kind of flight which is not achieved by the movement of the whole person in space but by regression or return to an earlier dedifferentiated state of organization — in other words, a flight through time. This is never complete, since ego psychic control still exists for the most part. However, certain old psychophysiological and conditioned or learned methods of communication are revived. These constitute part of the symptomatology that we call psychosomatic disturbances.

Both psychic and somatic systems of organization are homeostatically regulated processes, which means that an equilibrium occurs within ranges that are healthy and productive of total well being and functional efficiency. When a stimulus disturbs homeostasis apparently attempts are made to reverse the process or at least to maintain the disturbance within the healthy range. This may include heighened activity of one or more processes which take the brunt or the sacrifice of one or more functions as a sort of compromise adjustment.

Recently there has been an attempt to view the physiological disturbances associated with the regression in psychosomatic disease by means of language and concepts similar to those used for mental disorders. I spoke about forms of biological conditioning which are precursors to the predisposition toward the effect of pathogenic agencies. However, predisposing factors simply mean that personality, self, or ego as well as cells, organs, and organ systems seem to have various susceptibilities or, one might say, "awareness" of functional disabilities, if one can adhere to "pan-psychism." In the psychic sphere this may be evidenced by certain restrictions of perceptive systems which prevent crucial emotional stimuli from impinging on the organism. In the somatic system there may be special disturbances of secretions, excretions, or storage.

Because in any level of organization homeostasis represents a sacrifice of one level for the sake of a lesser evil — in other words, a compromise, a choice of alternative, in order to preserve other levels of the organization—that which may be maintained in a healthy state within the psychobiological organization is probably achieved at the expense of some disturbance which is less severe and more adaptive. In the same manner, the psychological defenses that are restrictive and disturbing to the organism are of lesser evil than the psychotic disintegrative effects of anxiety against which the defense often protects.

In the human subject, aside from the general alarm responses from the pituitary-adrenocortical axis, other endocrine responses appear less certain. Although we know that acute thyrotoxicosis is precipitated by rapidly appearing emotional crises, PBI changes are not usually found in the presence of brief anxiety states, anger, or induced stress responses. The same holds true with gonadal responses, although certainly the menstrual cycle, fertility in both males and females, and the course of pregnancy are influenced by disturbed emotions. The catechol amines should supposedly be involved in emotional processes, especially since anxiety seems akin to an epinephrine response and anger to that of norepinephrine, but their quantification in both plasma and urine has been technically difficult and, since their metabolism is so rapid, the timing of testing in relation to emotional display has been a problem in all but a few laboratories.

Other indirect indices such as hippuric acid excretion, cholesterol, ceruloplasmin, glucose, etc., are quantitatively related to the height of anxiety, but we know little about their place in the total economy of the stress responses. Lately studies of energy transfer systems and their mobilization during stress have opened up an area of considerable interest. It is contended that an increased activity of adenosine triphosphate (ATP) occurs with overwhelming anxiety and that the energy transfer is generally impaired in stressed schizophrenics. On the other side of the picture, much work is being done on the theory of toxic degradation products of catechol amines. Neither the deficient energy nor the toxic theory has been validated.

In the intact human being only indirect measurements can be made of organ responses. Aside from the ultrasensitive cardiovascular system, organs or systems respond in a variety of ways indicating no generally constant pattern. Respiratory functions, peripheral vascular tone, skin resistance, muscle tone, gastrointestinal motility, etc., respond in a variety of ways probably dependent on the particular pre-stress state and on their general patterned functioning laid down in periods of early development.

Neurophysiological activities correlated with emotions can be studied in animals, and many fruitful concepts have been applied to man. Hypothalamic activities are now not being viewed as discrete functions but as more general influences whose effects are dependent on peripheral states. Current research is oriented to higher levels of the brain, the limbic lobe which apparently has a profound influence on learning, memory, behavior, and endocrine functions. The central reticular structures seem to be concerned in general activating functions, and conversely in sleep, and are probably highly significant for our two psychiatric scourges, schizophrenia and melancholia. Clinically much information may be acquired, after the dust of overenthusiasm dies down, from the use of tranquilizing and energizing drugs on the physiology of emotions.

Clinically we have known that the anxiety organization is not simple. It encompasses a vast area of predispositions, a large number of privately meaningful predisposing factors, and a profound psychological and somatic disorganization. One would think, since anxiety is universal and under certain circumstances is more severe

only quantitatively, that it might be easily dealt with therapeutically. However, its defensive overlays, its social avoidance
behaviors, and its imprinting on the total organization often show
considerable stability. As a result, therapeutic procedures oriented
towards stability freed from anxiety are often unsuccessful.

I have already mentioned that there is a great disparity in time
between the stimulus and the anxiety response. The stimulus may
have occurred some weeks or days before, and the response may
come about only after a gradual build-up or the meaningfulness of
the stimulus may become apparent only after a weakening of defenses of denial. The component parts of the anxiety organization
have a relationship in time, a hierarchy, the kind of resiliency
which makes the development of a well-recognized causal chain
most difficult.

I have said that stress must be meaningful to the subject in
terms of either his predisposing physiological economy or the
nature of his psychic development. We thus might assume that
personality attributes are associated with a potentiality for different
patterned responses; but at present this subject, although we have
attempted to study it, is still much too complicated. We know that
personalities that have previously been conditioned to shame react
with anxiety most frequently at the possibility of impending
failure. Paratrooper trainees who were asked to drop fully protected from a small platform developed severe anxiety responses at
the possibility of not living up to the ego ideals of their fathers
or older brothers. On the other hand, in later phases of their
training, these same boys rarely failed to jump out of airplanes
without disabling anxiety.

Those persons who have a heavy load of guilt feelings react
most readily to threats of bodily harm. Others react to feelings of
impending disintegration more severely than either of the first
two mentioned. The threat of a social group's demand for conformity on the one hand or possible isolation by rejection on the
other are predisposing factors which indicate something about
previous personality associated with different susceptibilities. Determining these factors is often difficult because accompanying
anxiety are profound cognitive disturbances, expressed in diffi-

culties in decision-making and in severe distortions of perception. With these deficits, there is great difficulty in ascertaining the significance of the previous personality for the development of the stress response.

VI

This essay is intended as an introduction to the symposium which will take place tomorrow. It should serve only as a general statement of the mammoth ignorance that is characteristic of the field today despite centuries of philosophical considerations, careful clinical observation, and modern experimentation which is becoming greatly intensified in our time.

Mind-body unity, psychosomatic or comprehensive approaches, the unitary concept of man as a process within a total field in nature observable from many frames of reference, have been briefly mentioned tonight with the hope that the doctor who is involved in the diagnosis and treatment of diseases of man may understand thoroughly the complexity of affairs. This I have deliberately done as an antidote to the false simplification of stereotypes of so-called psychosomatic illness.

The point of view that I have presented indicates our ignorance, preserving for the physician many generalizations but only a few facts. By doing this, perhaps I have driven home a lesson which is of great importance. This is that, in the absence of adequate specific information concerning the effect of emotions on physiological processes, every individual with his previous somatic and psychological conditioning, with his particularly integrated psychosomatic pattern, with his alarm systems of varying thresholds, with his special interpretations of the meaningfulness of stimuli, and with his particular modes of defense against any aspect of disturbed equilibrium, constitutes a special problem. For example, an individual injected intravenously with epinephrine will subjectively experience among his many symptoms most of those he had previously known in any kind of previous stress situation. No matter what the conditions may be, stress response patterns seem to represent personal characteristics.

An individual can only be understood in his own right by a careful analysis of what made him as he is when he comes to the doctor complaining of illness. False stereotypes are not helpful. To the contrary, they have served to perpetuate or to instill a security which is unjustified.

For practical purposes the general global statements about holistic man are not facilitative for any therapeutic process, much less for any analytic approach. None of the specificity indications has been validated for etiology or diagnosis and they are, therefore, not helpful for planned therapy. Despite the search for groups of patterns or categories of people to lighten the load of diagnosis in therapy, none of them is sufficiently valid. Instead we must insist that the only way that one can adequately view an individual suffering from a psychosomatic illness is to know as much as possible about him as a person and about the story of his disturbance.

Knowledge in the head of the physician cures no one. We must ask a final and most disturbing question. Are there ways of curing patients suffering from psychosomatic illness? Are there methods for alleviating the pathology of emotions? There are many very helpful therapeutic procedures, but they do not encompass what in the nineteenth century were expected as cures. Methods of treatment require understanding of the best possible solution of the problem at hand with the encouragement and facilitation of whatever psychic defenses are necessary for any level of possible adaptation. This may mean increasing one person's defenses of a denial; for another, the utilization of illusions; for another, the adjustment to illness as an accepted fact; for still another, the avoidance of certain situations or relationships even at the expense of narrowing the patient's social participation, experience, or even creativity. It may mean the temporary safety-valve expression of feelings which require repetition from time to time, along with explanation and clarification. Perhaps eventually we will know the true value of tranquilizing and energizing drugs.

Certainly such supportive, directive, or manipulative therapy need not be frowned upon or depreciated, for the physician who wishes to help his patient has only three objectives in mind. He wants to make the patient feel subjectively better, he hopes to reduce the quantity or extensiveness of his symptoms, and finally he wishes to help the patient live better within the social group to which he belongs. These are modest goals. They should be striven for as far as possible, but the physician should not handicap himself with inferiority feelings, self criticism, and frustration because he can not reconstruct a personality or make it over. Neither can psychiatrists. No therapy makes new brain cells or new hearts or new limbs or new people. At best, some aspects of behavior can be modified by increasing the subject's capacity to learn. For the present let us be satisfied to do as much as possible while at the same time we attempt to learn from clinical observations and from scientific experiments what goes on in men under stress.

II

THE NEUROPHYSIOLOGIC CORRELATES
OF EMOTION

H. W. MAGOUN, Ph.D.

IT is appropriate indeed, in 1959, for the Annual Symposium of the Kaiser Foundation Hospitals to concern itself with the "Physiology of Emotion," for this is the Darwin Centennial year and Darwin made important contributions to our present understanding of emotion. A century ago, his classic work was published as *Origin of Species by Natural Selection, or The Preservation of Favored Races in the Struggle for Life.*[1] It proposed that the arrangement of living beings in an order of increasing complexity could be accounted for by natural selection working upon the range of normal variation, and so provided a materialistic explanation for the evolutionary scale of life.

From the contributions of this work, and from Darwin's later volumes[2,3] on *The Descent of Man* and *The Expression of Emotions* (Fig. 1), there can be synthesized the view that each living being adapted to its environment by staking out a territory in which it obtained food and so preserved its individual life, and sought a mate and reared its young and so preserved its race. In competition for survival, it was necessary for each form to defend its territory by aggressive combat or, when its enemies were overpowering, to preserve itself by flight. It was in relation to these basic biological activities, Darwin proposed, that the animal brain came to contain mechanisms for the management of what Mac-Lean[4] has more recently called the four F's: feeding, fighting, fleeing and — undertaking reproductive activity. Since these activities are obtrusively present throughout the animal series, the brain

26

mechanisms for them are obviously to be sought in the older, more primitive parts of the central nervous system. From a functional point of view, these life- and race-preserving neural mechanisms

FIGURE 1. Sketches from Darwin illustrating his principle of antithesis in THE EXPRESSION OF THE EMOTIONS (3). Note the contrasting positions of the head, trunk, tail and limbs in a dog "approaching with hostile intentions" (above) and one "in a humble and affectionate frame of mind" (below).

would seem to be related closely to the basic appetites and drives; in close relation to them, too, emotion would seem to be experienced as subjective feeling, and displayed peripherally as the coordinated behavior of glandular, visceral, and somatic effectors, which prepare or enable the animal to deal effectively with the evocative stimulation.

Knowledge of the neurophysiologic correlates of emotion first developed from investigation of these peripheral changes, described as emotional expression, and Lange and William James[5] went so far as to propose that perception of them was responsible for the emotional experience itself. Next, Cannon[6] showed that experimental induction of these peripheral alterations did not provoke emotion, nor did their peripheral block prevent it. Cannon proposed, instead, a primary mechanism in the cephalic brain stem, the upward discharge of which subserved the subjective aspects, while its discharge downwards evoked the expressive manifestations of emotional behavior. Important succeeding developments included the designation by Papez[7] of a neuroanatomical circuit for emotion (fig. 2), which interrelated basal forebrain structures with

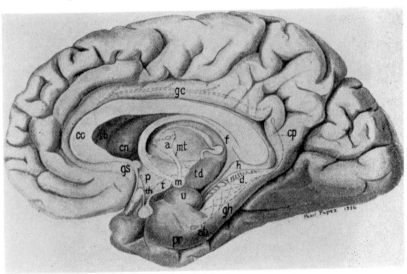

FIGURE 2. A neuroanatomical circuit for emotion, proposed by Papez (Arch. Neurol. & Psych. Papez, Oct. 1937).

the diencephalon and limbic portion of the cerebral hemisphere, bordering its attachment to the brain stem; and the physiological investigations of the Yale School (Fulton,[8] MacLean,[9] Kaada,[10]

Pribram and Kruger,[11]) supporting Papez' proposal. Still more recently, application of the techniques of ablation, stimulation, and recording the electrical activity of parts of the brain have each made further contributions supporting and extending these earlier general views.

After chronic ablation of the neocortex, Bard and Rioch[12] found that cats were still able to display coordinated patterns of emotional behavior, particularly those of anger. Because such activity was undirected and often inappropriately related to the environment, it was termed "sham" rage. The easy evocation of this behavior and its exaggerated display suggested that deeper lying mechanisms related to emotion may normally be inhibited, as well as excited, by higher levels of the brain. A number of more recent studies point to reciprocal feed-back relations for excitation and inhibition within these neural systems (Ingram,[13] Schreiner and Kling,[14] Green, Clemente, and De Groot,[15] Hugelin and Bonvallet,[16] Grastyán *et al.*[17]).

Other work has explored the coordinated emotional responses which can be elicited by stimulating these neural regions through electrodes chronically implanted in the intact brain. Affective-defensive responses were induced by Hess,[18,19] who proposed that these patterns of emotional display were so realistic (Figs. 3, 4) and might be related so specifically to external objects that they should not be described as "sham." More recently, excitation of these brain regions has been found to be negatively reinforcing of behavior. Such stimulation may serve as an unconditioned stimulus in the establishment of a conditioned reflex (Cohen, Brown, and Brown[20]). Additionally, if trained to do so, an animal may perform a task to prevent the stimulation of this part of its brain (Delgado, Roberts, and Miller,[21] Olds,[22,23] Lilly[24]).

By contrast, when electrodes are implanted in other areas of the basal mechanism, the animal may spend all of its waking time stimulating its own nervous system (Olds and Milner,[23] Lilly,[24] Brady[25]). Such activity may reach the fantastic rates of 8000 self-stimuli per hour (Figs. 5,6) and display modification upon manipulating the intensity of external drives for feeding or sexual activity (Olds[22]). From scattered verbal reports during stimulation of such

The Physiology of Emotions

brain regions in man, pleasant or unpleasant feelings may be experienced (Sem-Jacobsen[26]); and it may be recalled that the auras of temporal lobe epilepsy are often of this nature (Williams[27]).

FIGURE 3. Affective-defensive reactions induced by stimulation of the diencephalon through implanted electrodes. From Hess, W. R.: Hypothalamus and Thalamus. Documentary Pictures. Stuttgart, Georg Thieme, 1956.

These findings suggest the existence of neural mechanisms, possibly organized as dual, reciprocally-antagonistic half-centers, for the positive and negative reinforcement of behavior, with relations to the pleasant or unpleasant affective qualities of emotional excitement. This possibility has an interesting historical association with

Darwin's[3] principle of antithesis in the expression of emotion, illustrated by his sketches of the contrasting aspects of a dog "approaching with hostile intentions" and one in "a humble and affectionate frame of mind" (Fig. 1).

Most recently, observations obtained by recording the electrical

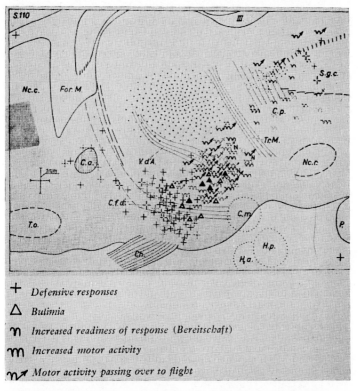

+ *Defensive responses*

△ *Bulimia*

ⁿ *Increased readiness of response (Bereitschaft)*

ₘ *Increased motor activity*

ₘ⁷ *Motor activity passing over to flight*

FIGURE 4. Parasagittal section through the cephalic brain stem of the cat, with symbols marking sites from which responses indicated were evoked. From Hess, W. R.: *Diencephalon, Autonomic and Extrapyramidal Functions.* New York, Grune & Stratton, 1954. Reproduced by permission.

activity of the brain during emotional behavior have made contributions in this field. The first synthesis was undertaken by Lindsley[28] in an activation theory of emotion. In the electroencephalogram recorded from the cerebral neocortex, Lindsley identified a pattern of low-voltage fast discharge, called "EEG arousal," as accompanying emotional behavior in both animals and

The Physiology of Emotions

man; and, in man, who can report verbally, during anxiety as well. Lindsley proposed that the brain mechanisms subserving this EEG pattern could display a continuum of activity ranging from initial

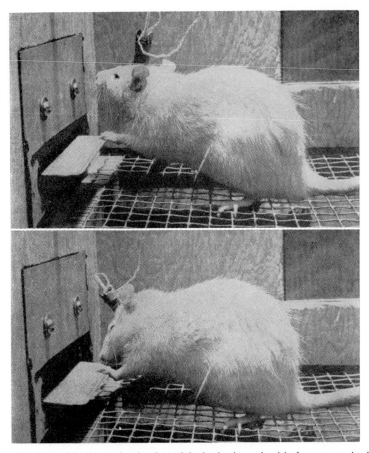

FIGURE 5. Rat with electrodes implanted in its brain and with foot upon the bar (above), presses bar (below) and delivers stimulus to its own brain. Although there is no display of pleasurable emotion (by contrast with the affective-defensive responses of Fig. 3), some animals have stimulated themselves for 24 hours without rest and as often as 8,000 times an hour. From Olds, J.: Pleasure centers in the brain. *Scient. Am.*, *195*:105-117, 1956.

alert attention, through tension and anxiety, finally to pronounced emotional excitement. This concept, of important relevance, has been extended by the succeeding recording studies of Green and

Arduini[29] and others, which have identified in the hippocampal paleocortex a contrasting kind of electrical discharge during the arousal state (Fig. 7). This pattern of hippocampal arousal consists

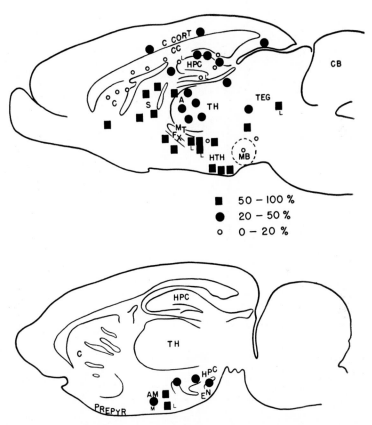

FIGURE 6. Parasagittal sections through the rat brain showing the distribution of implanted electrodes in self-stimulation experiments. The percentage figures were derived by counting periods of 30 seconds or longer without stimulation as intervals of no response. From Olds, J.: A preliminary mapping of electrical reinforcing effects in the rat brain. *J. Comp. & Physiol. Psychol., 49*:281-285, 1956.

of large slow waves, at 5-7 per second, called the theta rhythm. Its study has come to attract more attention as a central correlate of emotion than the arousal pattern in the neocortical record.

A second pattern of electrical activity in the basal forebrain, which similarly appears to be correlated with emotional behavior.

The Physiology of Emotions

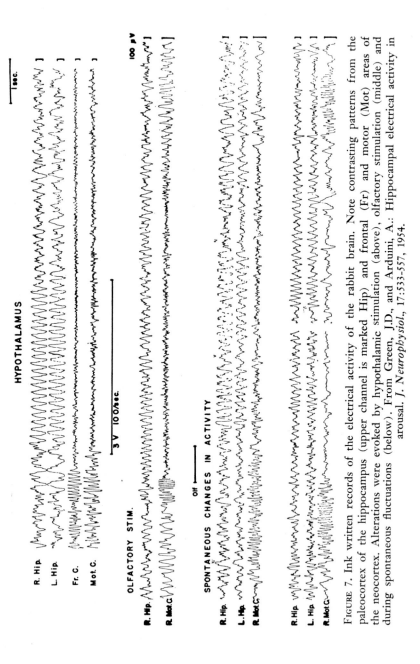

Figure 7. Ink written records of the electrical activity of the rabbit brain. Note contrasting patterns from the paleocortex of the hippocampus (upper channel is marked Hip) and frontal (Fr) and motor (Mot) areas of the neocortex. Alterations were evoked by hypothalamic stimulation (above), olfactory stimulation (middle) and during spontaneous fluctuations (below). From Green, J.D., and Arduini, A.: Hippocampal electrical activity in arousal. *J. Neurophysiol.*, 17:533-557, 1954.

has more recently been identified in records obtained from the amygdala by Lesse[30] and others. In this basal ganglion of the old forebrain, bursts of 40 per second activity are frequently, if not invariably, associated with excited behavior. In Lesse's records from four animals (Fig. 8) are seen the differing records of amygdaloid activity in natural sleep, during alert wakefulness, and

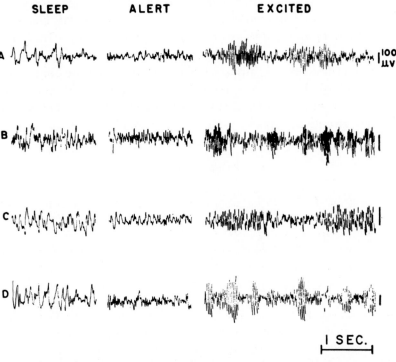

SLEEP   ALERT   EXCITED

FIGURE 8. Ink written records of the electrical activity of the basolateral portion of the amygdaloid nucleus of four cats, illustrating changes seen during states of sleep, alertness and excitement. Note bursts of 40-50/second activity during excited behavior [From Lesse (30)].

when the animal is excited. In each case, bursts of 40 per second discharge can be observed to characterize the excited state. Two structures of the old forebrain, the hippocampus and the amygdala, thus display characteristic patterns of electrical discharge with seeming relationship to emotional excitement.

With these important initial developments, the field of electrical recording of the brain's activity during its participation in reproductive and infant-rearing behavior (Sawyer[31]) and in operant, approach, or avoidance conditioning (Rusinov and Rabinovich,[32] Gastaut,[33] Rowland,[34] Galambos, Sheatz, and Vernier,[35] John and Killam,[36] Worden,[37] Grastyán, Lissák, Madarász, and Donhoffer,[17] Adey[38]) is expanding rapidly and promises significant further contributions to our understanding of the neurophysiologic correlates of emotion. In this connection, the final sentence of Darwin's *Expression of the Emotions in Man and Animals*[3] is as fresh and relevant today as in 1872:

"From these several causes, we may conclude that the philosophy of our subject has well deserved the attention which it has already received from several excellent observers, and that it deserves still further attention, especially from any able physiologist."

REFERENCES

1. Darwin, C. R.: *The Origin of Species by Means of Natural Selection, or The Preservation of Favored Races in the Struggle for Life.* London, 1859.
2. Darwin, C. R.: *The Descent of Man and Selection in Relation to Sex.* London, 1871.
3. Darwin, C. R.: *The Expression of the Emotions in Man and Animals.* London, 1872.
4. MacLean, P. D.: Contrasting functions of limbic and neocortical systems of the brain and their relevance to psychophysiological aspects of medicine. *Am. J. Med., 25:*611, 1958.
5. Lange, C. G., and James, W.: *The Emotions.* Baltimore, Williams and Wilkins, 1922.
6. Cannon, W. B.: *Bodily Changes in Pain, Hunger, Fear and Rage; An Account of Recent Researches into the Function of Emotional Excitement.* 2nd ed. New York, Appleton, 1929.
7. Papez, J. W.: A proposed mechanism of emotion. *Arch. Neurol. & Psychiat., 38:*725, 1937.
8. Fulton, J. F.: *Frontal Lobotomy and Affective Behavior: A Neurophysiological Analysis.* New York, W. W. Norton Co., 1951.
9. MacLean, P. D.: Psychosomatic disease and the "visceral brain";

recent developments bearing on the Papez theory of emotion. *Psychosom. Med., 11:*338, 1949.

10. Kaada, B.: Somato-motor, autonomic and electrocorticographic responses to electrical stimulation of rhinencephalic and other structures in primates, cat and dog; a study of responses from the limbic, subcallosal, or orbitoinsular, piriform and temporal cortex, hippocampus-fornix and amygdala. *Acta physiol. scandinav., 24 (suppl. 83):1,* 1951.

11. Pribram, K. H. and Kruger, L.: Functions of the "olfactory brain." *Ann. New York Acad. Sc., 58:*109, 1954.

12. Bard, P. and Rioch, D. McK.: A study of four cats deprived of neocortex and additional portions of the forebrain. *Bull. Johns Hopkins Hosp., 60:*73, 1937.

13. Ingram, W. R.: Brain stem mechanisms in behavior. *Electroencephalog. & Clin. Neurophysiol., 4:*397, 1952.

14. Schreiner, L. and Kling, A.: Behavioral changes following rhinencephalic injury in cat. *J. Neurophysiol., 16:*643, 1953.

15. Green, J. D., Clemente, C. D. and De Groot, J.: Rhinencephalic lesions and behavior in cats; an analysis of the Klüver-Bucy syndrome with particular reference to normal and abnormal sexual behavior. *J. Comp. Neurol., 108:*505, 1957.

16. Hugelin, A. and Bonvallet, M.: Étude expérimentale des interrelations réticulocorticales; proposition d'une théorie de l'assevissement réticulaire à un système diffus cortical. *J. physiol., 49:* 1201, 1957.

17. Grastyán, E., Lissák, K., Madarász, I. and Donhoffer, H.: Hippocampal electrical activity during the development of conditioned reflexes. *Electroencephalog. & Clin. Neurophysiol., 11:*409, 1959.

18. Hess, W. R.: *Diencephalon.* New York, Grune & Stratton Inc., 1954.

19. Hess, W. R.: *Hypothalamus and Thalamus: Documentary Pictures.* Stuttgart: Thieme, (Intercont. M. Bk. Corp.), 1956.

20. Cohen, B. D., Brown, G. W., and Brown, M. L.: Avoidance learning motivated by hypothalamic stimulation. *J. Exper. Psychol., 53:*228, 1957.

21. Delgado, J. M. R., Roberts, W. W., and Miller, N. E.: Learning motivated by electrical stimulation of the brain. *Am. J. Physiol., 179:*587, 1954.

22. Olds, J.: Self-stimulation of the brain. *Science 127:*315, 1958.

23. Olds, J., and Milner, P.: Positive reinforcement produced by electrical stimulation of septal area and other regions of rat brain. *J. Comp. & Physiol. Psychol.*, 47:419, 1954.

24. Lilly, J.: Learning motivated by subcortical stimulation: the start and stop patterns of behavior. Chapter 35 in *Reticular Formation of the Brain*. Henry Ford Hospital Internat. Symposium., Boston, Little Brown & Co., 1958.

25. Brady, J. V.: Temporal and emotional factors related to electrical self-stimulation of the limbic system. Chapter 34 in *Reticular Formation of the Brain*. Henry Ford Hospital Internat. Symposium., Boston, Little, Brown & Co., 1958.

26. Sem-Jacobsen, C. W.: Discussion. In Chapter 35 in *Reticular Formation of the Brain*. Henry Ford Hospital Internat. Symposium, Boston, Little, Brown & Co., 1958.

27. Williams, D.: The structure of emotions reflected in epileptic experiences. (Bradshaw lecture, abridged). *Brain*, 79:29, 1956.

28. Lindsley, D. B.: Emotions. Chapter in *Handbook of Experimental Psychology*. S. S. Stevens, Ed., New York, Wiley & Sons Co., 1951.

29. Green, J. D., and Arduini, A.: Hippocampal electrical activity in arousal. *J. Neurophysiol.*, 17:533, 1954.

30. Lesse, H.: Rhinencephalic electrophysiological activity during emotional behavior in cats. Chapter in *Explorations in the Physiology of Emotions*. L. J. West and M. Greenblatt, Eds. Washington, D. C., Am. Psychiat. Assn., Lord Baltimore Press, 1960. (In press.)

31. Sawyer, C. H.: Nervous control of ovulation. Chapter in *Recent Progress in the Endocrinology of Reproduction*. C. W. Lloyd, Ed., New York, Academic Press Inc., 1959.

32. Rusinov, V. S., and Rabinovich, M. Y.: Electroencephalographic research in the laboratories and clinics of the Soviet Union. *Electroencephalog. & Clin. Neurophysiol.*, Suppl. 8, 1958.

33. Gastaut, H., Jus, A., Jus, C., Morrell, F., Van Leeuwen, W. S., Dongier, S., Naquet, R., Regis, H., Roger, A., Bekkering, D., Kamp, A., Werre, J. Étude topographique des réactions électroencéphalographiques conditionées chez l'homme; essai d'interprétation neurophysiologique. Chapter in *Conditionnement et Réactivité en Electroencephalographie*. H. Fischgold and H. Gastaut, Eds. *Electroencephalog. & Clin. Neurophysiol.*, *9* (Suppl. 6):1, 1957.

34. Rowland, V. Differential electroencephalographic response to conditioned auditory stimuli in arousal from sleep. *Electroencephalog. & Clin. Neurophysiol.*, 9:585, 1957.

35. Galambos, R., Sheatz, G., and Vernier, V.: Electrophysiological correlates of a conditioned response in cats. *Science, 123:376,* 1956.

36. John, E. R., and Killam, K. F.: Electrophysiological correlates of avoidance conditioning in the cat. *J. Pharmacol. & Exper. Therap., 125:252,* 1959.

37. Worden, F. G.: Neurophysiological contributions to the understanding of schizophrenia. Chapter in *Schizophrenia; An Integrated Approach.* A. Auerback, Ed., New York, Ronald Press, 1959.

38. Adey, W. R.: Studies of hippocampal electrical activity during approach learning. Chapter in *Brain Mechanisms and Learning.* UNESCO, Springfield, Thomas; Oxford, England, Blackwell Scientific Publications Ltd. (In press.)

III

SOME ENDOCRINE STRESS RESPONSES IN MAN*

HUDSON HOAGLAND, Ph.D., Sc.D.

STRESS may be considered as any set of events which modify steady state conditions within the organism so as to activate homeostatic processes to adjust the internal environment. Thus a shift in blood acidity following exercise calls upon both chemical buffering systems and neurophysiological mechanisms to re-establish homeostasis. External temperature changes activate autonomic regulatory mechanisms to maintain constancy of temperature of the internal environment. The ingestion of chemical agents, foodstuffs in excess, or noxious agents likewise activates homeostatic processes and all of these events may be considered as stressful as they are reflected in measures of homeostatic adjustment.

Stress has a broader meaning for the organism in relation to its external environment. Any external situation threatening the organism may function as a stress. Thus activities of flight and fight with their concomitant psychological and physiological expressions of fear and anger are stressful. The processes of inhibiting fight and flight may result in stressful anxiety states. Psychological stress results from the intensification of instinctual drives and of the control of these drives to meet the demands of society. Such stresses may be chronic and produce far-reaching disturbances of

---

*A paper given at a Conference on Research on Stress in Relation to Mental Health and Mental Illness, held by the Mental Health Research Fund at Oxford in July 1958. It is to be published shortly, in the proceedings of that conference, by Blackwell Scientific Publications Ltd. under the title of *Stress and Psychiatric Disorder*.

40

a psychosomatic nature. The balancing of one's needs and satisfaction in terms of conscience represent stresses of this sort. The apparently same psychological stress situation may have quite different meanings for different persons in terms of their life histories and past conditionings so that attempts to objectify and standardize such stresses meet with great difficulty.

For the purposes of this discussion, I would like to limit considerations to responses of the adrenal cortex and adrenal medulla in man when stressed both by life situations and by experimental procedures in the laboratory which may call upon these endocrine systems to increase their outputs of hormones as measured by metabolic indices in the urine.

The studies to be reported deal primarily with investigations of our group at the Worcester Foundation and are concerned with responses of men to challenging situations both of a psychological and physiological nature. Since 1943 we have published a number of papers dealing with stress responses of the adrenal systems in normal men and in mental patients. Most of our work has been concerned with adrenocortical responses about which I shall have something to say, although time limitations preclude considerations of most of this material. I would like first to review some studies of my colleague, Dr. Fred Elmadjian, who in association with Dr. Justin Hope and Mr. Edwin Lamson has investigated the urinary excretion of epinephrine and norepinephrine in stressed individuals. At the time this goes to press most of these investigations have been published,[1,2] and the first part of this paper will summarize and paraphrase some of these findings. Elmadjian and his collaborators obtained data from normal subjects engaged in professional hockey playing and also from amateur boxers before and after fights. They also studied the excretion of epinephrine (E) and norepinephrine (NE) in psychiatric patients appearing at staff conferences. In addition they correlated data on E and NE excretion with a measure of hostility in a group of patients and finally obtained data on both therapist and patient during psychotherapeutic interviews.

From these studies will emerge the view that active aggressive, hostile behavior is accompanied primarily by the enhancement of NE excretion while anxious passive behavior primarily results in enhanced E excretion.

Appropriately timed urine samples collected before a stress and again after the stress were extracted for catechol amines by the alumina absorption method of von Euler and Hellner.[3] The maximum efficiency of this method yields 60-70% of the catechol amines based on recovery data. Bioassays on the extracts were performed by a modification of the method described by Gaddum and Lembeck.[4] This consists of testing the sample on the rat colon for NE and the rat uterus for E. The bioassay is based on the quantitative inhibition by the catechol amines of the contractions induced *in vitro* in a 2 ml. bath with acetylcholine. The inhibitions of NE and E are approximately equal when tested on the colon; but when tested on the uterus, E is 75 to 300 times more potent than NE. The colon assay was used when rapid estimates of total (NE + E) were desired.

To calibrate extraction and bioassay data in terms of E and NE excretion, Elmadjian carried out infusion experiments.[1,2] Figure 1 depicts the data of ten E infusions and nine NE infusions at rates of dosage of 0.05, 0.10, and 0.20 μg./kg./min. Pre-infusion

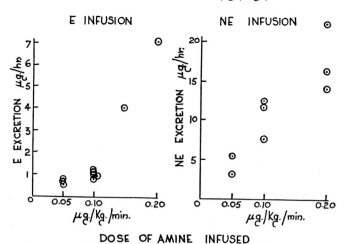

FIGURE 1. The excretion of epinephrine (E) and norepinephrine (NE) above control levels after 30-minute infusion of E and NE in doses of 0.05, 0.10, and 0.20 μg. per kilogram per minute (see text). (From Elmadjian *et al.*: *J. Clin. Endocrinol.*, 17:608, 1957.)

urine was collected from 9:00 a.m. to 10:00 a.m. at which time the infusion was started and continued for 30 minutes. The infusion collection represented urine collection ranging from 10:00 a.m. to approximately 11:00 a.m. The data in Figure 1 present the hourly excretion for each dosage rate above its control collection. In the case of E, only 0.5-1.0% of the total dose infused appears in the urine, while in the case of NE from 3.0-5.0% of the total dose is excreted in excess of the control sample. In the NE infusions the relationship of excretion rate to dosage is essentially linear. However, in the case of E infusion, there is a sharp change in the slope at doses above 0.10 μg./kg./min. While there is a two-fold increase in the excretion rate with the doubling of the dose from 0.05 to 0.10 μg./kg./min. there is a seven-fold increase in the excretion rate on subsequent doubling from 0.10 to 0.20 μg./kg./min. These data serve as a basis for estimating the approximate secretion rate of E and NE in the studies to be reported.

Studies of E and NE excretion showed marked diurnal rhythms. Table I presents data on the NE and E excretion during sleep

TABLE I. Diurnal Variation of Norepinephrine (NE) and Epinephrine (E) Excretion in Normal Subjects. (From Elmadjian *et al.: Recent Progress in Hormone Research, 14:*513, 1958.)

Sample Period[a]	NE (μg./hr.)	E (μg./hr.)
Study A (ten subjects)		
Sleep:	1.2	0.02
	± 0.12	± 0.002
Morning:	2.9	0.40
	± 0.48	± 0.10
Study B (six subjects)		
Sleep:	1.2	0.02
	± 0.14	± 0.01
Morning:	2.3	0.10
	± 0.49	± 0.02
Day:	2.4	0.21
	± 0.60	± 0.07

[a] See text for times of collection.

and waking states on ten normal subjects. Night samples of urine were collected during a period from approximately 10:00 p.m. to 6:30 a.m. and morning samples from 6:30 to noon. All subjects had breakfast and conducted their usual activities consisting of laboratory routines. Table I contains additional data on six normal subjects consisting of physicians and laboratory personnel who were conducting their usual daily activities. Each collected a sample representing the period of sleeping, a second sample from the time of waking to about 10:00 a.m., and a third sample from 10:00 a.m. to the time of retiring at night. There is seen a marked increase in the excretion rate of both E and NE during morning and day samples over that observed during sleep. The percentages of NE increases were smaller than values for E. For future reference we may note that morning and afternoon samples of E excretion have values ranging from approximately 0.1 to 0.4 μg./hr. per person; while NE values are from 2.0 to 3.0 μg./hr.

STUDIES OF ATHLETES

Hockey is a fast aggressive game, involving vigorous attack and defense. Studies were made of hockey players on a high grade professional team, the Boston Bruins. Timed pregame samples of urine were collected at ten to thirty minutes before game time, which was 8:30 p.m., and timed postgame samples were collected some three hours later. These latter samples included urine formed during the contest. Results from a number of games were studied. Table II lists values for pregame and postgame collections of the aggressive defensemen and forwards who do most of the skating. The data are presented in terms of creatinine values because it was not always possible to obtain properly timed samples. For samples taken following the game, there was a six-fold increase in NE excretion. Two players were sampled before the game, but on physical examination by the trainer, they were not permitted to participate. In the same table are presented the data on these players, indicating no postgame increase in NE but appreciable increase in E. Both players sat on the bench and watched the game. Both were concerned about their injuries and inability to play.

TABLE II. Excretion of Norepinephrine (NE) and Epinephrine (E) in Members of a Professional Hockey Team—Defensemen and Forwards versus Nonparticipating Players. (From Elmadjian *et al.: J. Clin. Endocrinol.*, 17:608, 1957.)

Urine Collection	Number of Hockey Players Sampled	NE (μg./100 mg. Creatinine)*	E (μg./100 mg. Creatinine)
Active hockey players (defensemen and forwards)[a]			
Pregame	20	2.7 ± 0.43	0.36 ± 0.07
Postgame	20	15.3 ± 2.20	0.95 ± 0.21
		t = 5.66	t = 2.68
		P = < 0.001	P = < 0.05, > 0.01
Two players who did not participate in the game[b]			
Pregame	1 (No. 18)	2.2	0.23
Postgame		3.3	0.75
Pregame	1 (No. 10)	5.6	0.78
Postgame		5.3	1.42
Player involved in fist fight			
Pregame	1 (No. 16)	3.5	0.18
Postgame		29.3	3.30

[a] The approximate hourly excretion is 10% less than the figure given in terms of 100 gm. creatinine when corrected by creatinine coefficient.

[b] Due to their physical condition.

———————

* Data in terms of micrograms per 100 mg. of creatinine may be computed in terms of micrograms per hour if the weight of the subject is known. Since the weight of athletes is highly correlated with muscle mass and creatinine excretion is dependent on muscle mass, the computation of the formula for creatinine coefficient would furnish the creatinine excretion per unit time for a particular weight (Kleiner, I. S., "Human Biochemistry," p. 317. Mosby, St. Louis, 1945).

$$\text{Creatinine coefficient (18-32 for males)} = \frac{\text{Mg. creatinine per 24 hr.}}{\text{Body wt. in kg.}}$$

For example, using a creatinine coefficient of 26, it was calculated that the subject weighing 200 pounds would excrete approximately 100 mg. per hour. Since the average weight of the hockey players was 180 pounds, the estimate in terms of micrograms per hour would be 10% less than that presented in terms of micrograms per 100 mg. of creatinine.

In Table II are also data on a player, #16, who showed a nine-fold increase in NE and a twenty-fold increase in E. He skated his regular turn, but did not play an outstanding game. At the end of the second period, however, he got involved in a violent fist fight with an opposing player and was ejected from the game.

The goal tender skates very little but is in constant vigilance in front of the net ready to defend the goal. The coach remains on the bench directing strategy. Data obtained on the goal tender in three games and on the coach in six games are presented in Table III. There was a marked increase in both E and NE excre-

TABLE III. Excretion of Norepinephrine (NE) and Epinephrine (E) in Goal Tender and Coach. (From Elmadjian *et al.: J. Clin. Endocrinol.*, *17*:608, 1957.)

Subject	No. of Games	Urine Collection	NE ($\mu g./100\ mg.$ Creatinine)	E ($\mu g./100\ mg.$ Creatinine)
Goal tender	3	Pregame	3.3 ± 0.7	0.45 ± 0.20
		Postgame	9.2 ± 1.8	1.30 ± 0.81
Coach	6	Pregame	1.8 ± 0.5	0.38 ± 0.09
		Postgame	3.7 ± 0.9	0.43 ± 0.21

tion in the goal tender but on the average there were no significant changes in the excretion of either amine in the coach. There were, however, individual games where the coach showed marked increase in E.

Another study was made on six amateur boxers competing in the finals of the Amateur Athletic Union boxing championship. Especial significance was placed on these three-round finals because the winners would thereby qualify for the final Olympic tryouts. A high state of expectancy characterized the fighters. This was reflected in the elevated E excretion rates observed in most of the prefight samples seen in Table IV.

On three fighters only one sample was obtained; on Ch and Wh the sample was a precontest collection. Both boxers showed elevated E excretion. Each showed ample evidence of tenseness and apprehension in the prefight interview. After the interview Ch went to the corner of the dressing room and shadow boxed

TABLE IV. Excretion of Norepinephrine (NE) and Epinephrine (E) in Amateur Boxers. (From Elmadjian et al.: J. Clin. Endocrinol., 17:608, 1957.)

Boxer	Urine Collection	NE[a] (μg.)	E[a] (μg.)	Outcome
Ch	Prefight	17.9	1.64	Winner by decision
	Postfight	—	—	in the third round
Sm	Prefight	38.1	1.78	Winner by TKO in
	Postfight	32.4	0.67	the third round
Pe	Prefight	6.7	0.22	Winner by decision
	Postfight	2.8	0.41	in the third round
Br	Prefight	4.2	0.40	Winner by decision
	Postfight	7.0	0.87	in the third round
Wh	Prefight	1.7	1.67	Winner by TKO in
	Postfight	—	—	the second round
Bra	Prefight	—	—	Loser by decision
	Postfight	15.9	1.70	in the third round

[a] Micrograms per 100 mg. creatinine.

for about five minutes, while Wh sat quietly on a bench with his trainer and refrained from shadow boxing before entering the ring. Ch, who shadow boxed, showed an elevated NE excretion, while Wh's NE value was low.

In general, high NE prefight values were noted in fighters who engaged in vigorous shadow boxing before the contest. The highest prefight E excretions were found in the fighters who showed the greater degree of anticipation preceding the fight. Increase in the postfight samples over the prefight samples of E were observed in those fighters who had to fight the distance for decision in close contests.

STUDIES OF NEUROPSYCHIATRIC PATIENTS

In ten psychiatric patients a study was made of the relationship between certain scores of the Malamud-Sands rating scale[2,5] and the excretions of E and NE. This scale rates the patient numerically in a number of categories. A designated baseline appears through the center of the rating scale and deviations from normality are estimated numerically. In comparing behavior characteristics with NE excretion, gradations of motor activity and gradations of hostility reactions were used and a composite score including only these two items of the Malamud-Sands ratings was used. Figure 2 shows the relationship of this score to NE excre-

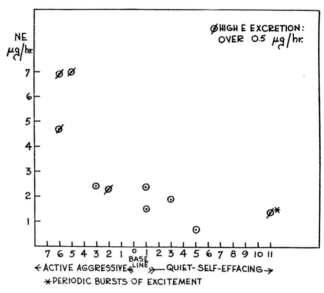

FIGURE 2. The relation of norepinephrine excretion to emotional state of neuropsychiatric patients. The abscissa depicts the composite score for the functions of motor activity and hostility reactions from the Malamud-Sands rating scale, and the ordinate represents the excretion of norepinephrine in micrograms per hour during the observation period. (From El-madjian *et al.*: *J. Clin. Endocrinol.*, 17:608, 1957.)

tion. Patients with active aggressive emotional display had higher NE excretion, while those with passive self-effacing emotional display had normal levels of NE. In this figure when a line appears through the circles, it indicates that these subjects also had a high excretion of E. The subject indicated by an asterisk had normal NE excretion, but the excretion of E was 2.75 μg./hr., which is extremely high. This subject showed periodic bursts of excitement with expressions of fear and guilt.

Studies also were made of neuropsychiatric patients during staff interviews. The patients are seated and are questioned by a psychiatrist before some twenty members of the hospital medical staff. The patient is aware that decisions about his continued stay in hospital will emerge from the interview. Eleven patients were studied by Elmadjian and his coworkers, on eight of whom control samples were obtained. The interviews took place in the mornings and the control samples were obtained at the same time on the next day. The results are shown in Table V. There were no

TABLE V. Staff Conference Interview of Neuropsychiatric Patients. (From Elmadjian *et al.: J. Clin. Endocrinol.,* 17:608, 1957.)

Sample	No. of Subjects	NE ($\mu g./hr.$)	E ($\mu g./hr.$)
Interview	11	2.6 ± 0.4	0.50 ± 0.14
Control	8	2.3 ± 0.2	0.27 ± 0.12
		NS	$P = < 0.001$

changes in NE excretion when the interview day was compared with the control. However, in every subject on whom a control was obtained there was an elevated excretion of E during the interview. As might be expected there were marked individual variations in this increase. The subjects in general were self-effacing and on their best behavior and showed no aggressive or active emotional display.

In another study urine samples were obtained from therapist and patient in a series of psychotherapeutic interviews carried on between 8:00 a.m. and 9:00 a.m. Samples were obtained before and after each therapeutic session as well as on control days during the same hours when neither subject was involved in a psychotherapeutic interview. Six psychotherapeutic sessions and six control days were studied. Urine samples were analyzed for NE, E, and 17-hydroxycorticosteroids. Figure 3 shows data on both therapist and patient. Along the abscissa are indicated the control values for both therapist and patient. Elmadjian, Hope, and Lamson[2] have described these results as follows:

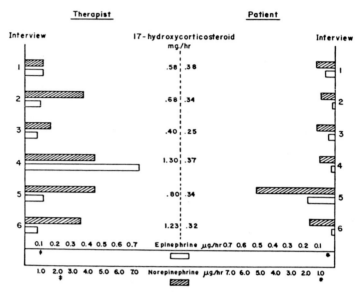

FIGURE 3. Data on therapist and patient during six psychotherapeutic interviews. Asterisk (*) indicates normal values for E and NE for patient. Double dagger (‡) represents normal values for therapist for same time of day when not engaged in psychotherapeutic process. Open bar indicates E excretion (micrograms per hour); hatched bar, NE excretion (micrograms per hour); 17-hydroxycorticosteroids of same samples given in center of figure as milligrams per hour. (From Elmadjian *et al.: Recent Progress in Hormone Research, 14:*513, 1958.)

"During the first interview we observed that both patient and therapist showed normal values during the psychotherapeutic session as compared to their control. In the second session a slight elevation is observed in the NE and 17-hydroxycorticosteroid excretion for the therapist with the patient still within normal limits for these determinations. In the third session the results indicate that all values are within normal limits. In the fourth psychotherapeutic interview, the samples indicated a twofold increase in the 17-hydroxycorticosteroid excretion with marked elevations for both E and NE for the therapist. The patient still showed normal values. In the fifth psychotherapeutic session we observe elevated 17-hydroxycorticosteroid values for the therapist accompanied by high values in NE, but E values returned to normal. However, we now observe the patient showing a marked increase in NE excretion with considerable elevation in E excretion, especially for this patient, with no increase in 17-hydroxycorticosteriods. In the sixth interview we note again a highly elevated 17-hydroxycorticosteroid excretion for the therapist with a moderately high NE value and normal E excretion. The patient's value shows an elevated NE, but E was back to normal.

"Information obtained from the therapist indicated that in the fourth session the therapist was severely criticized by the patient and the interview got 'out of hand.' The therapist was aware of his predicament subjectively and did admit an unpleasant emotional experience. In the fifth session, during the course of the psychotherapeutic interview the patient cried, showing considerable emotional expression. The therapist was quite concerned about the turn of events which had now taken an unexpected course with regard to the therapy. This aspect is again shown with the sixth session where the therapist again shows high values in 17-hydroxycorticosteroids and an elevated NE excretion.

"These data indicate that there is a possibility of studying by means of these measurements the emotional exchanges between therapist and patient during a psychotherapeutic process. From the physiological point of view it may also be noted that excretion of these substances during such an interview apparently reaches levels which are identified with stressful tasks such as . . . participation in athletics. These results again show that NE excretion under certain circumstances in the therapist or patient increase without an elevation in E, which further emphasizes the fact that these hormones may be differentially secreted, possibly depending on the nature of the emotional stress and the accompanying sympathicoadrenal responses."

We may summarize these findings of Elmadjian's group by pointing out that aggressive emotional displays accompanying stresses are related to increased excretion of NE with or without increased excretion of E. On the other hand, tense, anxious, but passive emotional responses are accompanied by increased excretion of E in association with normal excretion of NE.

The Physiology of Emotions

INDIVIDUAL DIFFERENCES IN RESPONSES IN RELATION TO PERFORMANCE OF STRESSFUL TASKS

I would like now to turn to some considerations of a different sort. These deal with individual differences in adrenal stress responses in normal men. In 1943 Pincus and I[6] reported a study of 17-ketosteroid excretion of army instructor pilots and civilian test pilots resulting from the stresses of flying airplanes and from operating a pursuit meter with airplane type controls. Timed urine samples were collected for several hours as controls before the flight or pursuit meter tests and again immediately after the test. The pursuit meter tests were conducted with different groups of men who operated the apparatus for either three or four hours. The urine samples were analyzed for 17-ketosteroids and usually increases in their output were found as a result of this relatively mild stress when the results of a number of runs for each individual were averaged. Since in a control study we found a diurnal rhythm for 17-ketosteroid excretion, corrections for this factor in relation to time of the test were made. Our published results showed that in general the higher a man's skill and the less his fatigue as measured by the decrement in his pursuit meter score, the less was his increase in 17-ketosteroid excretion following the test. It was as if the better performers needed to call less upon their adrenals to meet the situation. In this same study in a group of one-hour tests, air low in oxygen was breathed by the subjects during the pursuit meter operation. Performance was found to decline with the hypoxic conditions and 17-ketosteroid excretion was enhanced proportionally to the hypoxia. In a subsequent study, Elmadjian, Pincus and I[7] reported lymphopenia accompanying the rise in 17-ketosteroids with the combined hypoxia and pursuit meter stress.

The studies took into consideration the diurnal rhythm of adrenal activity first demonstrated by work from our laboratory. This is an important consideration since the diurnal rhythm may entirely mask adrenal responses to weak stresses. Thus 17-ketosteroid output for men in their twenties during the first two hours after waking increases 50% on the average over sleep levels and tends to fall throughout the day. Other adrenal cortical indices show similar rhythms. If afternoon poststress values of adrenocortical measures are compared with control values taken in the morning after rising, correction should be made for this rhythm. In general, for example, this amounts to an approximate average expectancy of 12% less 17-ketosteroid output for 1:00-3:00 p.m. samples compared to morning control collections.

We have carried out further pursuit meter studies with and without hypoxia and determined changes in eosinophils and in urinary 17-ketosteroids, epinephrine, norepinephrine, and electrolyte excretion resulting from the tests.[8] In this series we were especially interested in individual differences as measured by scoring ability in relation to the adrenal responses.

The pursuit meter studies in this series were carried out in twenty normal men divided into four teams of five men each. Each man was tested from eight to ten times, once per week, in runs lasting either two or three hours. Incentive was maintained by an hourly pay rate plus a substantial cash bonus graduated in terms of each man's scoring ability.

These pursuit meter studies have been concerned not only with the adrenocortical response as reflected in urinary 17-ketosteroids, Na, and K and in eosinophil changes, but we also measured effects of the stress on epinephrine and norepinephrine excretion. Total ketonic 17-ketosteroid determinations were made and urinary sodium and potassium were measured by flame photometry. The extraction and determination of urinary epinephrine and norepinephrine were carried out by Elmadjian according to the method already described. We regret that we were unable, because of other laboratory commitments at the time, to determine the 17-hydroxycorticoids.

In all cases timed pretest control and post-test urine samples were collected. The nature of these collections and of the test conditions for each team of five men has been described in detail in our publication of the data of the experiments.[8]

Team 1 underwent three hour pursuit meter tests but without hypoxia and with five-minute rest intervals at the end of each hour. This team was the least stressed. Team 2 with two-hour runs without rest and breathing on an average 13% oxygen was, as judged from their adrenal responses, more stressed than team 1. Members of teams 3 and 4 breathed air containing only 10.5% oxygen for two-hour tests also without rest intervals. Subjectively the men of teams 3 and 4 reported that they were very much stressed and considerable aftereffects were felt. One man of team 3 fainted in the course of one of the tests. Team 4 performed under conditions similar to those of team 3. Teams 3 and 4 averaged in age eighteen and seventeen years, respectively, while teams 1 and 2 were composed of older men with mean ages of thirty-two and twenty-six years, respectively.

Team 1 averaged 46% of the time on target. Team 2 averaged 40%, team 3 averaged 37% and team 4, 27%. While teams 3 and 4 operated under similar conditions, team 3 was more highly motivated and more competitive. It was composed of high school students who were part-time employees at the laboratory and had more interest in the study. Team 4 was made up of high school boys who came in at weekly intervals for the test. These average team scores, we believe, reflect the increasing stress effects under which the teams operated. Team 1 showed an average drop of only 11% in eosinophils while team 2 showed a drop of 20% and team 3 a drop of 43%. Team 4 showed an average eosinopenia of 38%. The eosinophil drops thus also indicate the ascending order of stress for teams 1, 2, and 3. Teams 3 and 4 were not significantly different in terms of eosinopenia responses.

Epinephrine and norepinephrine values were not obtained for team 2. In the other teams most of the men had, in three out of their eight to ten runs, urinary epinephrine and norepinephrine measured in both control and test samples. The mean increases over controls of urinary epinephrine for team 1 were 109% following the stress and for team 3 epinephrine increased by 208% on the average over control levels. Norepinephrine values of teams 1 and 3, however, increased by 54% and 32% respectively over pretest values. The less highly motivated team 4 showed epinephrine and norepinephrine increases of 170% and 125%, respectively. Since epinephrine increases represent increased activation of the adrenal medulla, these data further underscore the greater stress of teams 3 (208%) and 4 (170%) over team 1 (109%).

Increases in Na, K, and 17-ketosteroids resulting from the stress were much greater for team 2 than for the lesser stressed team 1.[8] But a curious discrepancy in these factors is seen in the cases of teams 3 and 4. Since the stresses of teams 3 and 4, who breathed an air mixture containing 10.5% oxygen, by all the above criteria were considerably greater than those of teams 1 and 2, we might expect the stress increases of Na, K, and 17-ketosteroids for these teams also to be greater, but actually the Na increases of team 3 were less than those for team 2 and in the case of team 4 Na, on the average, was retained. Potassium excretion showed an actual decrease over control levels following stress for teams 3 and 4 and 17-ketosteroids showed no increases for teams 3 and 4. This is contrary to the results for teams 1 and 2 where stress 17-ketosteroids showed significant increases of 18% and 48% respectively. These increases in stress 17-ketosteroids for teams 1 and 2 are in line with our previously reported findings in our pursuit meter studies for seventy normal men in this older age group.

There is, however, a marked age difference between the members of the first two teams and those of the third and fourth teams. The average age of team 1 is thirty-two years, that of team 2 is twenty-six years, but team 3 averages only eighteen years of age and team 4 averages seventeen years of age.

All of our previous stress studies have involved men over twenty. The failure of significant stress increase of 17-kestosteroids of the teams comprised of very young men, despite their big drops in eosinophils, is of special interest. It seems likely that the eosinophil decreases in teams 3 and 4 are mediated primarily by a large increased output of epinephrine rather than by adrenal corticoids in these younger groups. Clear evidence from our own and from other laboratories shows that persons who have experienced bilateral adrenalectomy show marked drops in eosinophils when injected with epinephrine.

Let us now compare the excretion of epinephrine and norephinephrine and 17-ketosteroid excretion in relation to eosinopenia. The data from team 1[8] indicate, in summary, enhanced excretion of epinephrine with the mild stress but relatively little eosinopenia or increase in 17-ketosteroid excretion. Teams 3 and 4 were more severely stressed as we have seen and our published data show the individual responses of these young men. The striking feature of the results is the relative absence of increase with stress of the rate of 17-ketosteroid excretion in these young men despite their eosinopenias. Though increases in NE were obtained in many of the experiments, the increases were not consistent and the results were quite variable. The eosinophil counts showed consistent decreases after the stress and the E excretion usually was increased. The decrease of the eosinophils was, on the average, 35% less than the control count, while the increased excretion of E averaged over 100%. One subject, however, showed no increase in E on all three occasions when he was subjected to the stress. It is of special interest that he is the identical twin brother of another member of this team. Adrenal cortical response measures were remarkably similar for these twin teammates, but the epinephrine and norepinephrine responses were very different.

In summary, under the conditions of these experiments, where subjects under twenty years of age underwent psychomotor stress under hypoxic conditions, the 17-ketosteroid excretion did not increase, the NE often did increase but not consistently. The eosinophils always decreased and E excretion usually increased following the stress. The stress eosinopenia appears to be correlated more often with E output than with 17-ketosteroid output. In six out of seventeen tests following stress, epinephrine excretion either did not change or it decreased with the fall of eosinophils. In three of these cases 17-ketosteroid excretion also did not increase with stress. The most striking case is that of one subject who showed large drops in eosinophils following stress in his three tests in which E and NE were measured but showed no significant changes in E, and in two of the three tests he showed declines in NE following stress. In only one of these three tests did his 17-ketosteroids increase. These results suggest that there may be a factor other than epinephrine, norepinephrine, or 17-OH-corticoids that may depress the eosinophils following stress. However, it should be borne in mind that adrenal steroids not metabolized to 17-ketosteroids and therefore not detected by our procedure may be involved in the eosinopenia, i.e., 17-desoxycorticoids such as corticosterone. Had we measured 17-OH-corticoids a clearer relation to the eosinopenia might have emerged.

Studies by Hill and his coworkers[9] of Harvard undergraduate rowing crews have shown rather small enhancements of 17-OH-corticoids and 17-ketosteroids with the stress of races. Their tests of cold exposure and one pursuit meter test also showed negligible adrenocortical activation either in terms of 17-OH-steroids or of 17-ketosteroids. In view of our pursuit meter findings we feel that these differences may be influenced by age factors. Age data for the Harvard undergraduates were not given but presumably their average age was under twenty. Our comparisons of groups of men twenty to forty and forty-one to sixty years old in several stress tests, including that of the pursuit meter, have shown no significant differences in mean per cent 17-ketosteroid stress responses between these age groups[10] but in the case of our teams 3 and 4 composed of boys sixteen to twenty years of age there is virtually no evidence of adrenal cortical response to our tests in terms of 17-ketosteroids or electrolyte responses. The seventeen-year-old subject on team 3 who fainted with hypoxia towards the end of one of his tests did not display enhanced 17-ketosteroid or electrolyte excretion on this occasion. His eosinophils dropped, however, by 60% and in the absence of evidence of adrenocortical stress we believe this effect was probably a result of enhanced epinephrine secretion. Unfortunately no epinephrine and norepinephrine determinations were made on this particular occasion.

Figure 4 shows a plot of the stress output of 17-ketosteroids over control levels as a function of age for the men in this study. A line has been run through the scattered points to indicate the trend with age. It is clear that the older men tend to call more upon release of adrenocortical precursors of 17-ketosteroids. Unpublished data on the analyses of the urine samples for their individual 17-ketosteroid contents lend support to this hypothesis. Etiocholane-2α, 11β-diol-17-one and etiocholane-3α-ol-11,17-dione excretion increased in the stress samples from team 1 but not from team 3. These substances are metabolites of hydrocortisone and cortisone. This is especially underscored by the fact that the older men were less stressed than the younger men by the conditions of

the pursuit meter tests. Were this not the case we might expect
the slope of the line to be steeper. Thus, team 1 operated without
low oxygen content and thus with less stress than did the younger
men of teams 3 and 4.

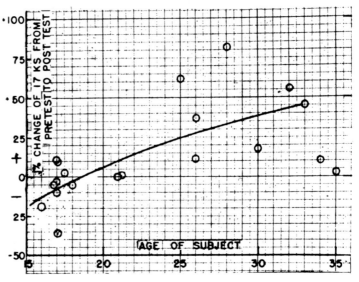

FIGURE 4. The stress output of 17-ketosteroids over control levels as
a function of age. (From Hoagland et al.: J. Appl. Physiol., 8:149,
1955.)

In our previous stress studies[1] we reported that the most efficient
performers on the pursuit meter were those showing the smaller
stress increases in 17-ketosteroid output. We suggested that these
more competent men needed to call less on the adrenal cortex to
meet the task. In our study the seventeen- and eighteen-year-olds,
while more stressed than the older men in terms of hypoxia and
lack of rest intervals, showed no evidence of adrenocortical stress
responses. The data of team 1 are of interest in demonstrating the
point that in comparing the individuals the better scorers showed
the smaller 17-ketosteroid responses to stress. In Table VI the
men of team 1 have been arranged from lowest to highest scorers
and the per cent increase in 17-ketosteroids with the stress is seen in
general to follow an inverse relationship to score. In column 3, we
give the pretest control levels of 17-ketosteroid outputs. One sees

that in general the higher pretest values are correlated with lower per cent stress increases. This indicates that pretest "tension" may be accompanied by better scoring and also by a smaller per cent rise in 17-ketosteroids from the already high pretest value. If the adrenal is working nearer its ceiling of activity before the test a

TABLE VI. Individual Rank Order of Scoring Ability and 17-Ketosteroid Excretion. (From Hoagland *et al.: J. Appl. Physiol., 8*:149, 1955.)

	1	*2*	*3*	*4*
			Corre-sponding	
		Rank Order	*Mean*	*Compari-*
	Rank Order	*Highest to*	*Values of*	*son Rank*
	Lowest to High-	*Lowest Per*	*Pretest*	*Orders,*
	est Final Mean	*Cent In-*	*17-ks,*	*col. 1 to*
	Score	*crease 17-ks*	*mg/hr.*	*col. 2*
Team 1				
1) *S. K.*	33	*S. K.* 45	0.54	1-1
2) *T. H.*	38	*T. H.* 18	0.45	2-2
3) *F. U.*	44	*F. U.* 11	0.69	3-3
4) *A. S.*	56	*N. G.* 11	0.68	4-5
5) *N. G.*	60	*A. S.* 3	0.72	5-4

lower per cent increase with stress is to be expected. Men "keyed up" for the test may be expected to give higher control pretest values since they are already under psychological stress. Such men may also be expected to perform better than the indifferent subjects. The data of Table VI are consistent with these interpretations.

The data of team 2 were not suitable for this type of analysis since the control samples were taken on days other than the stress days (but at the same time of day as the stress for purposes of correcting in this way for the diurnal rhythm). Thus no quantitative relationship existed between specific immediate pretest and post-test samples. Since teams 3 and 4 showed no adrenal cortical responses this analysis is also clearly not applicable.

A possible interpretation of the adrenocortical findings might be made as follows: suppose for example that the younger men excrete relatively large amounts of a 17-desoxy-C21-corticoid,

such as corticosterone and/or aldosterone, rather than 17-OH-
corticosteroids such as cortisol. Under these circumstances, Na
would be better retained, as indeed it is. Corticosterone is not
appreciably metabolized to 17-ketosteroid and their titer would
not increase with stress. Nor, had we measured 17-OH-corticoids,
would we have found much of an increase in these young men if
they tend to secrete relatively more 17-desoxy-C21-corticoids and
less 17-OH-corticoids. This situation might also apply to the
Harvard crew studies.[9] Do young men and those we have found
to perform best on the pursuit meter respond to stress with low
17-ketosteroid outputs because corticosterone replaces cortisol and
other 17-OH-steroids to some degree in their secretory products?
This question is unanswered but warrants further study.

In summary of these results — comparison of adrenal response
measures in normal men reflects the difficulty of the task as measured by scoring ability. Young men sixteen to twenty years of age
appear to call very little on adrenal cortical mechanisms to meet
stresses which enhance adrenocortical responses of older men.
Eosinopenia correlates better with the urinary excretion of
adrenalin than with that of 17-ketosteroids. Since eosinopenia may
occur in some stress cases with no evidence of enhanced adrenocortical and adrenomedullary activity, it is suggested that a possible
nonadrenal factor may be involved in the eosinopenia in addition to
the effects of epinephrine and the 11-oxysteroids. We have also
further evidence indicating that the better an individual's performance, the smaller is his per cent increase in 17-ketosteroid
output as a result of the stress. The data are at least consistent with
the view that young men and efficient performers tend to secrete
relatively more 17-desoxy-C21 steroids rather than 17-OH-corti-
coids.

I would now like to consider some recent studies from our
laboratories of Elmadjian, Lamson, Hope and Pincus (in press)
dealing with aldosterone excretion in anxiety states.

Urinary sodium retention accompanied with urine concentrations was noted by Elmadjian in a study of soldiers under combat
stress in Korea.[11] In this same study when test injections of ACTH
were administered to infantrymen after a prolonged stress of five

days of tough defensive action, no measurable increases in 17-hydroxycorticosteriod (17-OHCS) and 17-ketosteroid (17-KS) excretion were observed; however, there was a marked sodium retention. The pre-ACTH samples were also low in 17-OHCS and 17-KS values. The inference was drawn by Elmadjian and his colleagues in these postbattle cases that though the adrenal cortex was nonresponsive to ACTH with regard to 17-OHCS and 17-KS excretion, *the gland did secrete some hormone having potent sodium retaining activity*. Corticosterone and aldosterone were the two steroids considered as possible candidates, but neither of them nor their metabolites would be detected by methods used to measure 17-OHCS and 17-KS. More recently, Elmadjian *et al* (unpublished) and also Venning and her associates in Montreal have independently observed that in certain anxiety states there is an increased excretion of the powerful sodium retaining steroid, aldosterone. Thus Venning and Dyrenfurth[12] found that anxiety induced by presenting scientific papers at meetings, such as the one I'm giving now, and the taking of examinations increased the excretion of aldosterone without increasing that of 17-OH-corticoids. They found that 100 units of ACTH given to subjects produced a much smaller increase in output of aldosterone than did the taking of three-hour examinations. One subject showed a rise from 2 to 20 µg./24 hours following the presentation of a paper at a meeting.

Elmadjian and his coworkers have found a mean value of excretion of aldosterone of 4.1 µg./24 hrs. (range 2.4 to 4.8) for a group of nine normal subjects. Fourteen schizophrenic subjects showed a wide range of values with a mean of 4.4 µg./24 hrs. (range 1.2 to 10.0). It was noted that eight of the fourteen samples from the schizophrenics showed values of 2.4 µg/24 hrs. or less. The excretion rate was not related to the acuteness or chronicity of the schizophrenia as far as could be seen but rather to the emotional state of the subject when sampled, the more tense, anxious patients excreting most aldosterone. A study of ten hospitalized patients diagnosed as suffering from anxiety neuroses showed marked elevations of aldosterone excretion. Six such patients excreted values of 10.0 to 12.5 µg./24 hrs. One, however, excreted a normal

value of 2.4. A patient with anxiety neurosis and depression excreted 10 μg./24 hrs., as did one with compensated malignant hypertension and anxiety state. Another hypertensive with anxiety
yielded a value of 8.0, as did a patient diagnosed as having an
anxiety neurosis and depression. A normal student after an oral
doctoral examination excreted aldosterone at a rate of 10.0 μg./24
hrs.

Some of the high aldosterone excreters showed low excretion
rates for 17-OHCS and normal amounts of 17-KS. It is of interest
that Albeaux-Fernet and his associates[13] reported that in chronic
asthenia they obtained low 17-OHCS excretion with low 17-KS.
They further observed that these subjects did not show increased
17-KS and 17-OHCS after ACTH injection. They presented data
indicating increases in 17-desoxy-C21 steroids. The inference
drawn was that corticosterone was the major adrenal cortical
steroid secreted in chronic asthenia. The similarity of these results
and the inferences drawn to those of the Korean study earlier
mentioned are worthy of note.

Elmadjian and his coworkers have presented the following
hypothesis relating to adrenal steroid biogenesis and metabolism as
an attempt to relate the various findings in adrenal steroid excretion
to stress, and especially explain, in part, the elevation of aldosterone
in certain anxiety states. The adrenal cortex in the first stage of
stress secretes 17-OHCS which are measurable by the Porter-Silber
reaction and some 17-KS which may be estimated by the Zimmer-
man reaction. As the stress condition continues either the adrenal
cortex ceases to show an increment of 17-OHCS with an increase
in 17-KS, or the 17-OHCS secreted are more rapidly metabolized
to 17-KS. As the stress is further sustained, both the excretion of
17-OHCS and 17-KS are low due primarily to inhibition of the
17-hydroxylating mechanism in corticosteroid biogenesis.

In summary, persons experiencing chronic or acute anxiety
appear to show changes in the nature of the adrenocorticoid output with a suggested tendency to favour aldosterone and possibly
corticosterone secretion rather than cortisol. Such an interpretation
has also been made in relation to battle-stressed cases and it may be
applicable in the stresses that have been described in studies of

younger men operating the pursuit meter under conditions of anoxia. Much more work needs to be done before these points can be considered established.

REFERENCES

1. Elmadjian, F., Hope, J. M. and Lamson, E. T.: Excretion of epinephrine and norepinephrine in various emotional states. *J. Clin. Endocrinol.*, *17*:608, 1957.

2. Elmadjian, F., Hope, J. M. and Lamson, E. T.: Excretion of epinephrine and norepinephrine under stress. *Recent Progress in Hormone Research*, *14*:513, 1958.

3. Von Euler, U. S. and Hellner, S.: Excretion of noradrenaline, adrenaline and hydroxytyramine in urine. *Acta physiol. scandinav.*, *22*:161, 1951.

4. Gaddum, J. H. and Lembeck, F.: The assay of substances from adrenal medulla. *Brit. J. Pharmacol.*, *4*:401, 1949.

5. Malamud, W., Hope, J. M. and Elmadjian, F.: Objective evaluation of therapeutic procedures in mental diseases. *Boston Med. Quart.*, *2*:1, 1951.

6. Pincus, G. and Hoagland, H.: Steroid excretion and the stress of flying. *J. Aviation Med.*, *14*:173, 1943.

7. Hoagland, H., Elmadjian, F. and Pincus, G.: Stressful psychomotor performance and adrenal cortical function as indicated by the lymphocyte response. *J. Clin. Endocrinol.*, *6*:301, 1946.

8. Hoagland, H., Bergen, J. R., Block, E., Elmadjian, F. and Gibree, N. R.: Adrenal stress responses in normal men. *J. Appl. Physiol.*, *8*:149, 1955.

9. Hill, S. R., Goetz, F. C., Fox, H. M., Murawski, B. J., Krakauer, L. J., Reifenstein, R. W., Gray, S. J., Reddy, W. J., Hedberg, S. E., St. Marc, J. R. and Thorn, G. W.: Studies on adrenocortical and psychological response to stress in man. *A.M.A. Arch. Int. Med.*, *97*:269, 1956.

10. Hoagland, H., Pincus, G., Elmadjian, F., Romanoff, L., Freeman, H., Hope, J., Ballan, J., Berkeley, A. and Carlo, J.: Study of adrenocortical physiology in normal and schizophrenic men. *A.M.A. Arch. Neurol. & Psychiat.*, *69*:470, 1953.

11. Pace, N., Schaffer, F. L., Elmadjian, F., Minard, D., Davis, S. W., Kilbuck, J. H., Walker, E. L., Johnston M. E., Zilinsky, A., Gerard, R. W., Forsham, P. H. and Taylor, J. G.: *Physiological*

Studies on Infantrymen in Combat. Calif. University Publications in Physiology, Vol. X, No. 1, Berkeley, University of California Press, 1956.

12. Venning, E. H. and Dyrenfurth, I.: Effect of stress on the excretion of aldosterone. (Abstract) *J. Clin. Endocrinol.*, *16:*961, 1956.

13. Albeaux-Fernet, M., Bugard, P. and Romani, J. D.: Excretion of urinary corticoids in conditions of chronic asthenia. *J. Clin. Endocrinol.*, *17:*519, 1957.

14. Kass, E. H., Hechter, O., Macchi, I. A. and Mou, T. W.: Changes in patterns of secretion of corticosteroids in rabbits after prolonged treatment with ACTH. *Proc. Soc. Exper. Biol. & Med.*, *85:*583, 1954.

DISCUSSION

Dr. William F. Ganong: Listening to the presentations last night and this morning, I have been impressed that little distinction has been made between data obtained in experiments on animals on the one hand, and observations of man, on the other. Although much valuable information can be obtained from both types of study, there are peculiar limitations and advantages to each. Experimenting with animals, one becomes acutely aware of the difficulties involved in categorizing emotional responses. The animals cannot communicate, cannot symbolize. Therefore, unless we take a frankly anthropomorphic approach, animal emotional responses can properly be described only in reasonably broad and basic terms. On the other hand, in animals it is possible to remove at least some of the multiple variables which determine the ultimate emotional response.

There are other differences in approaching the physiological basis of emotion between the psychologist and the psychiatrist on the one hand, and the neurophysiologist on the other. There is an old saw about what would happen if a psychologist and a neurophysiologist were presented with a typewriter and asked to determine the way the typewriter worked. The psychologist would pick up the pages that had been typed in the typewriter, the "productions" of the typewriter, and by reading these, would decide how the typewriter worked. The neurophysiologist would hit the machine with a hammer and then from looking at the pieces, attempt to decide how the whole had worked originally. After listening to Doctor Magoun's excellent discussion of the contributions of the "hammer school," I am beginning to wonder if the analogy is still appropriate. At any rate, the hammer has become a very small and delicate one. Perhaps it has been traded in for an electronic probe.

Experiments with physical restraint in animals illustrate this cruder but more direct neurophysiological approach. Doctor Hoagland has emphasized the potent stimulating effect of emotional "stress" on the adrenal cortex in man. Physical restraint produces an emotional response in animals[1,2] and among the objectively measurable concomitants of this stimulus is an activation of the adrenal cortex.

We became interested in this problem some time ago. Our initial experiments were performed using the simple expedient of tieing a dog to a board, but subsequently we constructed a more comfortable canvas sling device for routine studies. The sling is supported in a wooden stand, and the dog fits into it in much the same way that you or I lie in a hammock on a hot summer day (Fig. 1). Putting the animals in this device for two hours produced

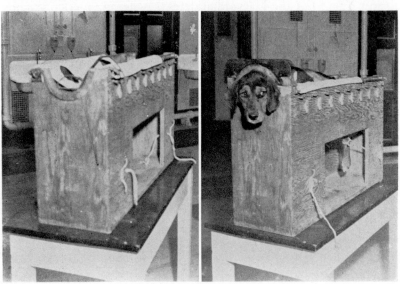

FIGURE 1. Immobilization stand.

a marked increase in adrenocortical secretion. However, many of the animals struggled while in the stand. Was this physical exertion, rather than the emotional trauma, stimulating the adrenal cortex? We attempted to answer this question by the seemingly simple experiment of exercising dogs. Animals were run on a treadmill and their adrenocortical function measured. Such exercise did produce adrenal activation. However, a certain understandable amount of coaxing and restraint was essential to induce the dogs to exercise on the treadmill. In this case, the animals were held in a loose harness, and accordingly, it was impossible to separate completely the factor of restraint from the exercise involved.

Hume and his associates[3] finally overcame this difficulty by studying that most ideal and available laboratory animal, the medical student. A group of students exercised vigorously on the treadmill and their adrenal function was measured. Here there was no problem of restraint or, presumably, of motivation. No increase in adrenocortical secretion occurred.

At about the same time, investigators in Thorn's laboratory made observations on the Harvard crew in their annual race against Yale.[4] For the Harvard athletes, rowing in practice sessions was not associated with appreciable increases in adrenocortical function. Rowing in the big race against Yale did cause marked adrenal stimulation. Significantly, however, both the coxswain and the coach showed the same degree of adrenal activation as the oarsmen during the race, although their only exercise was that involved in sitting in their respective boats and urging the crew on. Apparently, therefore, it was the emotional investment in the race rather than the muscular exertion which produced the endocrine activation. I was interested to hear Doctor Hoagland draw essentially the same conclusion on the basis of his analysis of other athletic contests.

Accordingly, it seems reasonable to conclude that it is not the struggling of the dogs in the canvas sling but the psychic component which is responsible for the observed adrenal response. In addition, some of our dogs do not struggle at all, but rather sit forlornly without moving for the two hour period; yet the degree of adrenal response in these animals is as great as it is in those which struggle violently. Finally, Bonvallet and his associates[1] showed that sectioning the spinal cord in the cervical region did not abolish the response.

Another question immediately arises: Will the animal adapt to repeated testing? I must emphasize that it is impossible to define "adaptation" in precise neurophysiological terms; but it does seem to be a valid question to ask whether or not the dog will "get used to" the stand and fail to show the adrenal response. We ruled out this possibility by immobilizing a series of four dogs on five consecutive days. The magnitude of their adrenocortical response, as measured by the peripheral venous 17-hydroxycorticoid level after two hours on the stand, was as great on the fifth immobilization as it was on the first. A typical experiment is shown in Figure 2. In this dog, the pre-immobilization corticoid values show an

EFFECT OF REPEATED IMMOBILIZATION ON
PLASMA 17-OH CORTICOID LEVELS
IN THE DOG

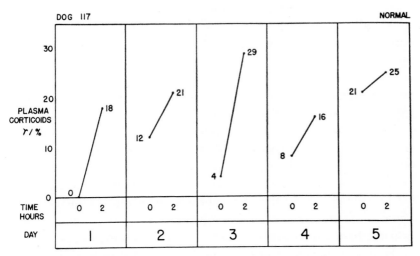

FIGURE 2. Response to immobilization on five consecutive days.

interesting tendency to rise with each succeeding test. Does this represent a beginning conditioned response in terms of adreno-

cortical discharge, the animal responding to the preparations in-
cident to putting him in the cage? This point deserves further
investigation.

At any rate, immobilization is a reproducible stimulus, and
because it increases adrenocortical secretion, we have a peripheral,
but convenient and objective end point. Furthermore, it evokes
an emotional response. How can it be used to study the physiological basis of emotions?

One way is to study the effect of immobilization on the chemical
content of the brain. The hypothalamus contains a large amount
of serotonin, a substance suspected of being a mediator for synaptic activity in this part of the brain. The role of this substance
in mediating the effects of tranquilizing drugs on the one hand
and of psychotogenic agents such as lysergic acid diethylamide
on the other is the subject of considerable debate. There has been
an immense amount of pharmacological research relating to serotonin, but very little attention has been paid to the effects of non-
pharmacological stimuli. My associate, Mr. Halevy, and I have
studied the effect of immobilization on the serotinin content of the
hypothalamus and find that this stimulus produces a slight but
statistically significant rise in the hypothalamic content of this
amine.[5] Whether or not this biochemical change is meaningful in
terms of the physiology of emotional expression, or indeed if it is
specific for emotional as compared to physical "stress" remains to
be determined. I bring it up as an example of one line of physiological research which can be pursued with profit.

Another approach is that of making lesions in various parts of
the brain and seeing how such destructive interference affects the
response to immobilization. Observing the modifications of emotional responses produced by destructive lesions was mentioned
by Doctor Magoun. It is an approach which is definitely rem-
iniscent of the hammer and the typewriter, but it can provide
valuable basic information. Some years ago[6,7] we found that lesions
in the most ventral part of the hypothalamus, the median eminence,
blocked the adrenocortical response to immobilization (Fig. 3).
Such a lesion is not selective, and also blocks the response to such
physical stimuli as surgical trauma. This and other evidence has

led to the conclusion that the region of the hypothalamus immediately above the pituitary gland is a sort of funnel, a final common
pathway by which a great variety of afferent impulses from the

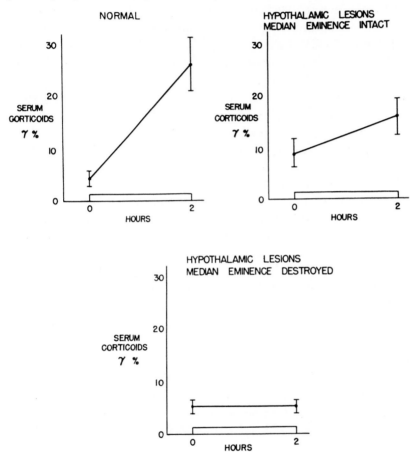

FIGURE 3. Effect of brain lesions on the immobilization response. (From *Comparative Endocrinology*, A. Gorbman, Ed., New York, John Wiley & Sons, Inc., 1959, with permission.)

brain converge to initiate secretion of adrenocorticotropic hormone by the adenohypophysis.

In another series of experiments, a decline in circulating blood
eosinophils was used as the indicator of adrenal activity. In forty
normal dogs, the eosinophils fell 66.2 ± 2.1% (mean ± standard

error of the mean) four hours after the start of immobilization in the canvas sling. Hypophysectomy (five dogs) and adrenalectomy (seven dogs) but not adrenal demedullectomy (five dogs) abolished the response. Median eminence lesions blocked the response to this stimulus and to operative trauma. However, in five animals with lesions in the anterodorsal portion of the hypothalamus, the adrenal response to immobilization was abolished, while the response to surgical trauma remained intact. No area was common to the lesions in these five dogs, but taken together, the lesions covered the area between the region of the anterior commissure and the middle of the median eminence. This suggests that they interrupted afferent pathways descending into the hypothalamus from the limbic cortex.

Finally, Dr. Elaine Smulekoff and I had the opportunity to study four male dogs in which the amygdaloid nucleus had been destroyed bilaterally. Because of the current interest in possible endocrine effects of such lesions, I think it is worth mentioning that we found testicular weight and histology, thyroid radioactive iodine uptake and histology, and adrenal histology normal. These dogs showed a normal hypertrophic response of the remaining adrenal after unilateral adrenalectomy, and their eosinopenic response to operative trauma was also normal. On the other hand, their circulating blood eosinophils fell only $22.7 \pm 11.1\%$ four hours after immobilization. This figure is significantly different from the mean fall in normal dogs at the 1% level. These data suggest that the neural impulses initiating ACTH secretion in response to immobilization pass from the amygdaloid region through the anterior and dorsal hypothalamus to the median eminence.

The observations also may have broader implications. It is interesting that the behavioral analysis in the amygdaloidectomized dogs indicated an absence of the behavior normally associated with fear. A similar effect has been reported by others.[8] In the canvas sling, certainly part of the emotional response of normal dogs is one of fear. Is it possible, therefore, that amygdaloid lesions somehow inhibit the emotion of fear; hence the effects of fear, including increased adrenocortical activity, are not seen?

Plasma concentration of epinephrine and norepinephrine in hemorrhagic and anaphylactic shock. *Am. J. Physiol., 190:*310, 1957.

19. Garcia, H., and Wallace, J.: Plasma concentrations of epinephrine and norepinephrine in normal individuals, with observations on the arteriovenous difference and *in vitro* disappearance of the amines. *Proc. Am. Soc. Clin. Invest.*, Atlantic City, May 6, 1957, p. 28.

20. Cohen, G., and Goldenberg, M.: The simultaneous fluorimetric determination of adrenaline and noradrenaline in plasma. II. Peripheral venous plasma concentrations in normal subjects and in patients with pheochromocytoma. *J. Neurochem., 2:*70, 1957.

21. Manger, W. M., Schwarz, B. E., Baars, C. W., Wakim, K. G., Hollman, J. L., Petersen, M. C., and Berkson, J.: Epinephrine and arterenol (norepinephrine) in mental disease. *A.M.A. Arch. Neurol. & Psychiat., 78:*396, 1957.

22. Regan, P. F., III, and Reilly, J.: Circulating epinephrine and norepinephrine in changing emotional states. *J. Nerv. & Ment. Dis., 127:*12, 1958.

23. Mason, J. W., and Hamburg, D.: Unpublished observations.

24. Elmadjian, F., Hope, J. M., and Lamson, E. T.: Excretion of epinephrine and norepinephrine in various emotional states. *J. Clin. Endocrinol., 17:*608, 1957.

25. Ström-Olsen, R., and Weil-Malherbe, H.: Humoral changes in manic depressive psychosis with particular reference to the excretion of catechol amines in urine. *J. Ment. Sc., 104:*696, 1958.

26. Rothballer, A. B.: The effects of catecholamines on the central nervous system. *Pharmacol. Rev., 11:*494, 1959.

27. Weil-Malherbe, H., Axelrod, J., and Tomchick, R.: The blood-brain barrier for adrenaline. *Science, 129:*1226, 1959.

28. Kety, S. S.: Biochemical theories of schizophrenia. Part I of a two-part critical review of current theories and of the evidence used to support them. *Science, 129:*1528, 1590, 1959.

29. McDonald, R. K.: Problems in biologic research in schizophrenia. *J. Chronic Dis., 8:*366, 1958.

30. Szara, S., Axelrod, J., and Perlin, S.: Is adrenochrome present in the blood? *Am. J. Psychiat., 115:*162, 1958.

31. Raab, W.: Specific sympathomimetic substance in the brain. *Am. J. Physiol., 152:*324, 1948.

32. Udenfriend, S., and Creveling, C. R.: Localization of dopamine-β-oxidase in brain. *J. Neurochem.*, 4:350, 1959.
33. Spector, S., Prockop, D., Shore, P. A., and Brodie, B. B.: Effect of iproniazid on brain levels of norepinephrine and serotonin. *Science*, 127:704, 1958.
34. Carlsson, A., Lindqvist, M., and Magnusson, T.: 3,4-Dihydroxyphenylalanine and 5-hydroxytryptophan as reserpine antagonists. *Nature*, 180:1200, 1957.
35. Elkes, J.: Pharmacologic influences on affect and behavior. (This volume, p. 95.)

DISCUSSION

Dr. Alan Goldfien: It is quite apparent from Dr. Kety's presentation that the recent studies of the pathways of biosynthesis and degradation of epinephrine and norepinephrine have provided us with a far greater understanding of these processes. Furthermore, important advances in our understanding of autonomic function should result from the use of biochemical tools provided in these studies. It is, however, just as clear that in some areas which are of interest to this symposium, thought has not been deterred by the availability of reliable observation. In these areas careful experimentation and critical evaluation are no less important.

During the past five years evidence has been accumulating which has led some investigators to conclude that norepinephrine is a specific hormone of the adrenal medulla in the sense that it is secreted by cells differing from those secreting epinephrine and that these cells are innervated by pathways with specific central representations. Expressions of this idea have led to the commonly held theory that the adrenal medulla will respond by secreting the hormone that is best suited to reverse the disturbance which resulted in the increase in secretion. The evidence advanced in favor of this hypothesis has in some instances been criticized but the greatest problem has been one of interpretation. This is well illustrated by the histological studies of Hillarp and Hökfelt.[1] These investigators by means of histochemical technics reported that staining differences existed among the cells of the adrenal medulla. On the basis of these studies, the authors concluded that epinephrine and norepinephrine were stored in separate cells. Even if we assume that their observations support this conclusion, which we cannot do without reservation, it is not possible to conclude that a cell storing norepinephrine will secrete norepinephrine since, as pointed out by Dr. Kety, norepinephrine is the precursor for epinephrine in the normal biosynthetic process.

Another building block in this structure was provided by investigators who reported that hypothalamic stimulation resulted in variations in the proportion of norepinephrine secreted by the adrenal medulla. Folkow and von Euler,[2] who measured the epinephrine and norepinephrine content of the adrenal venous

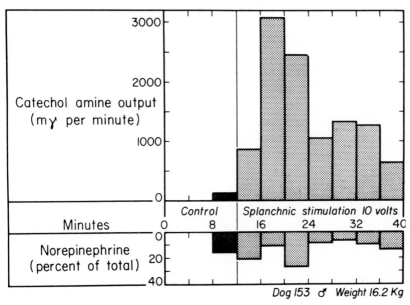

Dog 153 ♂ Weight 16.2 Kg

FIGURE 1. Effect of direct stimulation of the splanchnic nerve on adrenal medullary secretion.

blood of the cat during hypothalamic stimulation, were able to find considerable variations in the quantities of each of these amines when different areas were stimulated. However, in thirty experiments an increase of norepinephrine greater than that of epinephrine was found in only two instances. The interpretation of some of the variations in the proportions of the two amines which are observed may be difficult. This is well illustrated by the experiment reported in Figure 1. In this study, adrenal venous blood was collected before, during, and after direct continuous electrical stimulation of the distal end of the severed splanchnic nerve. We found that over a period of twenty-eight minutes the proportion of norepinephrine in the sample varied from 5 to 25% although the character of the electrical stimulus remained unchanged.

Several years ago Dr. Ganong and I embarked upon a series of studies which we hoped would provide a more secure basis for evaluating this problem. The rate of the adrenal medullary secretion of epinephrine and norepinephrine was measured during hypoglycemia, pentobarbital and ether anesthesia, laparotomy, carotid occlusion, and hemorrhage. In addition, we stimulated 73 areas in the dienchephalon and its neighboring structures, the spinal cord and the splanchnic nerve. None of these studies yielded convincing evidence in support of the concept of preferential norepinephrine secretion by the adrenal medulla. In general, we found that the greater the rate of secretion, the greater the percentage of epinephrine.

The findings in another group of experiments, in which asphyxia was employed as the stimulus to adrenal secretion, were in marked contrast to these. In a typical study illustrated in Figure 2, the trachea was clamped after several samples of adrenal venous blood had been obtained. Following clamping there was a rapid rise in the total secretion, which is illustrated in the upper half of the figure. Concomitantly, the proportion of norepinephrine greatly increased. The increase in the proportion of norepinephrine was not always maintained throughout the period of asphyxia, suggesting that two mechanisms of secretion might be involved. Further studies, in which nervous connections to the adrenal medulla were interfered with by a variety of procedures, have not completely eliminated the response of the adrenal medulla, confirming reports from several other laboratories that in the absence of innervation, anoxia and cyanide release amines from the adrenal. These studies have not progressed

sufficiently to enable us to support or to contradict the role of
the nervous system in this qualitatively different response.
However, Comline and Silver[3] observed comparable changes

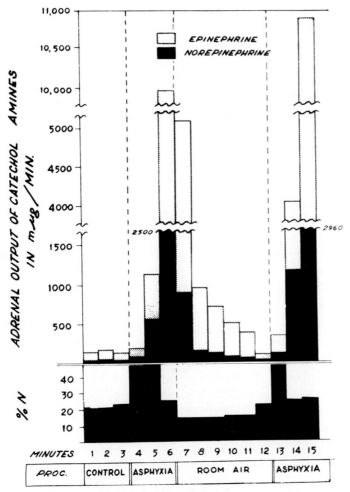

FIGURE 2. The rate of secretion of epinephrine and norepinephrine by
the adrenal medulla in asphyxia. Norepinephrine is plotted as percent
of total amines secreted on the lower half of the figure.

after denervation of the adrenal medulla of the sheep fetus,
suggesting that this alteration may be independent of nervous
control. I feel that there is not a great deal of valid evidence

available to support the hypothesis of specific differential secretion, at least in the dog.

In man the problem of differential secretion has been studied in a somewhat different context. The inability to obtain adrenal vein blood with ease has prevented the direct approach to the problem. However, in view of the results of studies quoted by Dr. Hoagland, most investigators are willing to use plasma and urine epinephrine concentrations as an indicator of adrenal medullary activity, and norepinephrine concentrations as an indicator of adrenergic nerve activity. It has been suggested, nevertheless, that regardless of the source, the secretion of epinephrine and of norepinephrine have specific emotional correlates. As noted earlier in the symposium, hostile aggressive behavior has been said to be associated with an increase primarily in norepinephrine in urine and plasma; whereas fear and anxiety may be associated with an increase in epinephrine.

In a group of normal subjects under basal conditions, the average plasma norepinephrine level was 1.5 ± 0.5 μg./ml. In a similar group of subjects working at their routine activities in a laboratory, the amount was more than double: 3.7 ± 1.7 μg./ml. Just as marked effects have been reported to follow the assumption of the upright position. In a rather extensive investigation by Tage Sundin,[4] the urinary excretion of norepinephrine was more than doubled by change of position on a tilt table from supine to $75°$. Many additional studies of physical exercise have shown an increase in norepinephrine excretion. The amount of exertion involved is different from that which characterizes marathon running, hockey, etc., which are associated with a rise in the level of both epinephrine and norepinephrine.

These observations are also borne out in a study (Fig. 3) which we carried out on patients receiving electroshock therapy,[5] who invariably responded with a striking increase in both norepinephrine and epinephrine in plasma. In the group of patients yielding the data shown in Figure 3, the seizures were modified by succinylcholine and thiopental; the points are plotted with relationship to the amount of modification of the seizure by these drugs. A rather close correlation was obtained; muscular activity was associated with a rise, suppression of muscular activity even with a fall in the plasma levels of norepinephrine.

Since aggressive behavior and rage are associated with increased muscular activity, it is to be expected that evidence suggesting an increase in norepinephrine secretion may be found. For the same

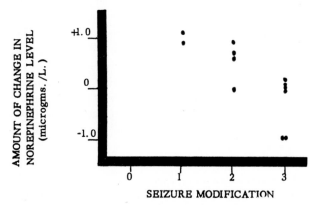

SEIZURE MODIFICATION

FIGURE 3. Relationship of degree of seizure modification and change in norepinephrine level. (From Havens *et al.*: Catechol amine responses to electrically induced convulsions in man. Chapter 10 in *Biological Psychiatry*. J. H. Masserman, Ed., New York, Grune & Stratton, Inc., 1959.)

reason this change need not, and on the basis of current information probably cannot be considered a specific emotional correlate.

We have also been interested in secretion of norepinephrine by the brain, as a possible source of evidence for its function in the nervous system. Several years ago, Doctors Ganong and Aronow removed the pituitary gland from dogs and compared the epinephrine and norepinephrine levels in portal venous blood with those in femoral arterial blood. They were able to find an increase in the portal vein plasma epinephrine levels, but carried out only a few experiments. We have conducted a series of experiments on six dogs subjected to stress after the implantation of a cannula in the cavernous sinus, and were not able to demonstrate a difference between the levels of norepinephrine or epinephrine at that site and in the peripheral circulation. It is apparent, however, that the newer technics for measurement of the metabolic products of the active amines must be applied to these studies before definitive information can be obtained.

REFERENCES

1. Hillarp, N. A., and Hökfelt, B.: Evidence of adrenaline and noradrenaline in separate adrenal medullary cells. *Acta physiol. scandinav., 30:55*, 1953.
2. Folkow, B., and von Euler, U. S.: Selective activation of noradrenaline and adrenaline producing cells in the cat's adrenal gland by hypothalamic stimulation. *Circulation Res., 2:191*, 1954.
3. Comline, R. S., and Silver, M.: Response of the adrenal medulla of the sheep foetus to asphyxia. *Nature 181:283*, 1958.
4. Sundin, T.: The effect of body posture on the urinary excretion of adrenaline and noradrenaline. *Acta med. scanidav., 161 Suppl. 336:1*, 1958.
5. Havens, L. L., Zileli, M. S., Dimascio, M. A., Boling, L., and Goldfien, A.: Catechol amine responses to electrically induced convulsions in man. In *Biological Psychiatry*. J. H. Masserman, Ed., New York, Grune & Stratton, Inc., 1959.
6. Personal communication.

V

DRUGS INFLUENCING AFFECT AND BEHAVIOR: POSSIBLE NEURAL CORRELATES IN RELATION TO MODE OF ACTION

J. ELKES, M.D.

"It is interesting to notice that the different nervous centres of the body manifest elective affinities for particular poisons . . . That medicinal substances do display these elective affinities is a proof, at any rate, that there are important intimate differences in the constitution or composition of the different nervous centres, notwithstanding that we are unable to detect the nature of them; and it may be we have in these different effects of poisons on the nervous system the promise of a useful means of investigation into the constitution of the latter."[1]

IT is curious, yet in keeping with all we know of him, how this passage, written by Henry Maudsley nearly one hundred years ago should set the theme of much that is new and fresh in the pharmacology of the brain and of behavior — a subject which, by way of uneasy travail, is slowly transforming a terrain of empirical natural history into the growing edge of a new science. It does so by resolving more and more into the disciplines which compound it; and equally, by compelling, as does no other branch of the neurological sciences, a fusion of these various disciplines. It ranges from behavior, including the swift nonverbal transactions of thought, to the neural substrate of behavior. This, indeed, is a wide span. Yet it is the steady extension of the subject to the limits of its cognate disciplines which, already, is leading to the evolution of a pharmacology of behavior of total organisms very

95

different from a pharmacology preoccupied with the behavior of tissues and organs. In these advances — empirical and experimental — the action of drugs on the affective systems has taken pride of place. Man's feeling states obtrude themselves incessantly in his social transactions, and have consistently compelled a seeking out of means for their attenuation or enhancement or change. The tranquilizers and stimulants are as old as alcohol and opium, tea or coffee. Familiarity, however, has blunted our curiosity about these old established remedies; and many excellent reviews already cover the agents which have come down to us in recent years in empirical profusion.[2,3,4,5,6] It is therefore the limited purpose of this paper to examine some correlates of the action of psychotropic drugs which may bear upon their influence on the affect systems and which — to borrow Maudsley's phrase — may perhaps shadow out some trends for future enquiry. These correlates will be considered at the neuroanatomical, electrophysiological, and neurohumoral levels.

I. NEUROANATOMICAL CONSIDERATIONS: THE SUBORGANIZATION, INTERCONNECTEDNESS AND MUTUAL OCCLUSIVENESS OF THE SYSTEMS SUBSERVING AFFECTIVE BEHAVIOR

The steady shift in emphasis from the form and function of the cerebral cortex to a mounting emphasis on subcortical centers has singled out three, or perhaps four, systems which, as emphasized by other speakers,[7] by mutual interplay steer the patterns of affective behavior in the discharge of their adaptive, homeostatic functions. The systems in question are the hypothalamus, the reticular activating system, and the rhinencephalic formation; with perhaps a fourth group, the caudate and lentiform masses (the so-called "corpus striatum") now moving into focus also. Each of these has received its share of extensive review,[8,9,10,11,12,13,14,15] but in the case of each, cumulative experience with a variety of techniques has steadily emphasized three separate, though related, trends. The first is the discrete neuroanatomical and cytological suborganization of these systems; the second, the interconnectedness of elements within these systems with each other, and with relatively distant elements at high cortical and high spinal level; and the third, the reciprocal, complementary, yet mutually occlusive relationship which some patterns and modalities represented in these systems bear to each other. These trends may be relevant when considered against the action and the mode of action of drugs on these systems.

There is little doubt in the light of even older studies of the anatomical inhomogeneity and cytological differentiation of the hypothalamus.[8,9,10] Similarly, more recent studies have emphasized a remarkable anatomical and cytoarchitectonic[16,17] differentiation within the reticular activating system[18] where, as Olszewski put it, "the variety of cells found within a few cubic centimeters of the mesencephalon . . . is greater than in any other part of the central nervous system".[19] The elements entering into the paleocortical and subcortical structures which comprise the so-called "limbic system",[13] show similar differentiation. Each of the systems thus encompasses a mosaic of subsystems, which, in a manner only poorly understood at present, are related and fitted into each other.

This understanding, however, is being steadily enhanced by the connections now being established between the various subsystems, and between them and various regions of the cortex. These connections are reticulofugal as well as reticulopetal, corticofugal as well as corticopetal. Rich connections have been shown to exist between a widespread area in the mesencephalon, and the hypothalamus.[20] These projections originate in the ventral part of the periaqueductal grey substance, including Gudden's dorsal tegmental nucleus, and the paramedian and medial tegmental cell groups. They extend to the hypothalamus by way of the dorsal longitudinal fasciculus of Schutz (which terminates in the periventricular region of the hypothalamus) and the system of the mammillary peduncle (which, though feeding principally into the mammillary body, also projects to the lateral region of the hypothalamus, as well as to the preoptic and septal regions). The lower midbrain, so richly exposed to nonspecific ascending afferent influences, is thus put into a direct connection with areas bearing upon endocrine and autonomic regulation. It is, incidentally, also of interest that direct projections from the more rostral midbrain tegmentum travel to the caudate and lentiform nuclei. The story of these latter structures, and their relation to behavior, remains to be written.

The above pathways, connecting the midbrain with the hypothalamus however, find their descending counterpart in the rich and varied connections of the limbic system to the midbrain. Their description forms a landmark on the subject.[21] The projections are both direct and indirect. The direct hippocampo-mesencephalic projections distribute only to the rostral part of the central grey substance. The indirect hippocampal pathways "in part interrupted by further relays, and probably also representing indirect projections of the amygdaloid complex, originate in the septum and in the lateral preoptic and hypothalamic regions, as well as in the mammillary body. Such pathways reach the midbrain in three fibre systems, viz., the medial forebrain bundle, the fasciculus retoflexus, and the mammillo-tegmental tract. Each of these three bundles has a dual distribution in the midbrain: part of their fibres terminate in extensive central lateral regions of the tegmentum, while the remaining component distributes to various subdivisions of a paramedian midbrain region encompassing the ventral part of the central grey substance, Tsai's ventral tegmental region, interpeduncular nucleus, Bech-terew's n. centralis tegmenti superior, and Gudden's dorsal and deep tegmental nuclei."[22]

Three points emerge from the above studies. First, they demonstrate a striking and reciprocal two-way apposition of the connections linking the limbic forebrain structures with midline areas in the midbrain; the arrangement amply justifies the term "limbic system midbrain circuit",[21] introduced to describe this two-way path. Secondly, it is well to note the inordinately widespread efferent routes emanating from this system. These "escape pathways,"[21] over and above the closed loops already mentioned, include projections to the medial hypothalamic region, to the anterior and intralaminar nuclei of the thalamus, as well as the diffuse ascending and descending conduction systems of the midbrain tegmentum. Thirdly, the septal and lateral preoptic regions and the medial hypothalamus would appear to be specially placed in this intricate reciprocal arrangement. Both are nodal areas, for the septal area shares primary projections from the hippocampus and the amygdala, and projects on to the midbrain by way of the medial forebrain bundle and, less directly, by way of the stria medullaris, the habenula, and the fasciculus retroflexus. The medial hypothalamic region receives (downward) fibres from the limbic forebrain structures via the stria terminalis as well as the bundle of Schutz. Short fibres from the same circuit probably connect with the supraoptic nucleus of the hypothalamus. Thus, on anatomical grounds alone, the septal and hypothalamic regions are in a peculiarly favorable position to balance and translate influences within the limbic-midbrain circuits into endocrine and visceromotor responses. The suborganization of the paleocortical structures,[12,13,14,23] their differential responsiveness (in terms of latency) following electrical stimulation of the amygdala,[24] and their role in behavioral motivation have been recently fully reviewed.[25,26] Here, again, one is impressed by the richness of the afferent connections of the limbic-midbrain system and the limited, fast, cable-like efferent connections which it forms with the midline areas known to mediate affectively charged motor responses. In a way yet poorly understood this system would appear to be intermediate between the discrete analysis of diverse signals at "high" level and the discharge of the limited, genetically coded, stereotype responses known as affective behavior. It appears to participate in both, and to modulate the wide range of one against the limited repertoire of the other. It is possible that this limbic-midbrain circuit may play a part in the several simultaneous transactions concerned with the apposition and matching of new information against motivationally charged stored patterns; in determining the positive (appetitive) or negative (aversive) connotation of a given stimulus situation; and in mediating the discharge of the most appropriate affective responses. The speed at which these transactions occur must presumably be very high.

There is, however, a third feature which characterizes the organization of the deeply ingrained, genetically coded response patterns which participate in the operation of the motivational systems. This is their reciprocal, mutual occlusiveness, despite a close juxtaposition of cell assemblies which subserve and selectively release them. That this is a fairly general principle is apparent in the older findings on the distribution of the cell groups subserving temperature control in the diencephalon,[27] where the opposing modalities of heat loss (vasodilation and increased respiration) and heat conservation (vasoconstriction, release of epinephrine) appeared to be regulated by an interplay between elements situated within a short distance of each other. The central neural regulation of food intake shows a similar pattern. The demonstration of "appetite" and "satiety" centers within the hypothalamus[28] suggests the existence of closely related mechanisms for the initiation and for the suspension of eating behavior, and a mutually appropriate interlocking of these two mechanisms. In the areas of motor activity and patterns of emotional expression, a series of major and now classical stimulation studies[29] has defined the so-called "ergotropic" areas, concerned with increased motor excitability, activation of respiration, rise of blood pressure and pulse rate. These have been contrasted with the so-called "trophotropic" areas leading to inhibition of motor activity, diminution of muscle tone, slowing of respiration, and fall in blood pressure. Whereas the former are principally distributed in a relatively broad area of the posterior subthalamus, posterior hypothalamus, and anterior midbrain, the latter is more likely to be encountered in the anterior hypothalamic field, and an area between the habenulointerpeduncular tract and the mammillothalamic bundle. The same studies also drew attention to the predominantly sympathetic autonomic responses associated with stimulation of the ergotropic areas, and the predominantly parasympathetic responses elicited by stimulation of the trophotropic areas. Yet caution has to be exercised in an unqualified acceptance of this distribution. The parameters of electrical stimulation are important and in certain instances (such as lower frequencies of stimulation) may, for example, elicit parasympathetic effects in the posterior (ergotropic) areas of the hypothalamus,[30] or elicit both parasympathetic and sympathetic discharge[31] upon stimulation of an area. The recent extension of these stimulation studies to self stimulation techniques[32] has further contributed towards a broad topography of the so-called "motivational systems." In the rat, the positive motivational systems[33] include most of the rhinencephalic cortex as well as part of the thalamus, tegmentum, and basal hypothalamus. The negative motivational system is far smaller. It invades the subthalamus and the dorsal hypothalamus, and its relationship to the recognized pain systems is far from clear. It is difficult at present to assess the full physiological meaning of these far reaching studies. Their important implications, though recently considered,[34] require further step-by-step enquiry. They do, however, suggest a broad binary grouping of the patterns of affective behavior, and also the possibility of a discrete suborganization of other patterns within this double frame of reference. Discrete stimulation studies[35,36] have demonstrated the fractionation of such patterns, and the remarkable way in which one "bit" of behavior can be selected and made to manifest out of context with the program of behavior of which it is part. It is obvious that to serve the adaptive purposes for which they were presumably intended, these various subsystems must be guided in their comprehensive performance by further integrating systems. These have been sought particularly at the paleocortical level, whose contribution to the control of motivational systems has recently received comprehensive review.[25,26] The cumulative evidence is in places contradictory. Yet it strongly suggests that elements in the limbic system can both restrain and activate the patterns of discharge associated with affective behavior. Mentioned here may be the early and lucid studies on the influence of temporal lobe deficits on emotional behavior in monkeys[37]; these studies included lesions in the frontotemporal cortex, the pyriform lobe, the amygdaloid complex, the presubiculum and the hippocampus. Equally important were the ablation studies in the cat[38] which furnished strong suggestive evidence of the role of the amygdaloid complex or the cingulate gyrus, or both, in restraining gross affective discharge in the neodecorticate preparation. In these, as in subsequent series[39,40] species differences loomed large. They did,

however, stress the modulating function of discrete and highly
localized areas in the rhinenecephalic formation on the patterns
of emotional expression and, moreover, drew attention to the
association of some areas with the discharge of broadly pleasurable
responses. Recent studies in which chemical stimulation (by means
of locally applied crystals of carbaminoylcholine) was substituted
for electrical stimulation[41] have particularly emphasized this
aspect. These demonstrated a high incidence of enhanced pleasure
and grooming reactions following the induction of discharges
from the hippocampus, as against a low incidence following
chemical stimulation in other regions. Taken in conjunction with
the anatomical evidence cited above it is possible to subsume,
in a tentative and far from satisfying way, the existence of two
systems concerned respectively with pleasurable or aversive
behavior. What, however, has to be constantly borne in mind
is the remarkable balance between excitation and inhibition, tonic
restraint and release, which operates in these delicate and swiftly
changing equilibria. It is difficult to speak of diffuse influences in
systems which sweep and in places overlap and interlock with
one another in this remarkable way. Overactivity and underactivity, attack or avoidance, "pleasure," or "fear," or "in-
difference" may apparently play and flow into each other
according to delicate shifts in balance in certain nodal cell groups.
The septal region, the median eminence of the hypothalamus,
the periaqueductal grey, and other as yet unidentified regions
may comprise nodal points in maintaining these equilibria. Yet
we know little of the switchgear and the discriminate and selective
gating mechanisms which quite automatically operate within the
various systems in arriving at the appropriate homeostatic response.
As in the case of other modalities (for example, muscle tone, or
posture, or fine voluntary movement), the deliberate selection
(by experimental intervention) of one "bit" of behavior from
a larger repertoire in no way reflects the elegance, smoothness,
and flow of the normal operation. What normally manifests,
what finally is selected out, or, as we say, what we "experience"
represents in fact, a final common path. Yet the activation of
such an affective response, and the genetically programmed cell

assembly which subserves it, is presumably preceded, within fractions of a second, by several simultaneous transactions involving the temporal apposition, convergence, and coding of neural patterns at widely separated topographical levels. It may, for example, involve the taking in of sensory cues (or the activation of a memory trace); the analysis and matching of these in terms of cognate traces, or, as we say "experience"; a grouping and further condensation of these transforms in terms of their appetitive (YES) or aversive (NO) connotation; and the final activation of the appropriate motor-somato-endocrine response. The reasons for mentioning these aspects here are, first, to point to the dependence of the affective response on the *history* of the nervous system at any particular time: what it will put out will, to a large extent, depend on what it has "experienced"; and secondly, to show that pharmacological interference at the level of final common path of response can be but one of several ways in which a drug may influence motivational behavior. The stages preceding the final response may be as important as the response itself.

There is one last point which will be briefly considered, inasmuch as it may bear upon the interplay and balance between the various subsystems comprised within the affective apparatus. It has been known for some time that motor activity and a number of autonomic functions may be subject to periodic and self-limiting fluctuations. Thus, for example, in the rat,[42] activity and food intake show regular four to five day peaks, coinciding with oestrus. This stable and rhythmic behavior, however, is markedly distorted by even a single exposure to severe stress, such as forced swimming or prolonged fighting. The five-day cycle is replaced by a cycle very much longer (of the order of 20 to 22 days); food intake is markedly increased, though its relation to motor activity is inverted. There is marked increase in weight; and there are signs strongly suggestive of hypothalamic and pituitary involvement. A pituitary tumor has been described in such cases.[42]

A single severe stress thus appears capable of producing irreversible damage in an area which, as almost no other, acts as a governor or regulator of autonomic discharges. One wonders what the role of these cell masses and of those feeding into them, in the adaptation to stresses of a more mundane, more subtle, and more clinical nature, may be. For the present, blood hormones, and particularly 17-hydroxycorticoid levels, most readily reflect these responses; and here again, an interaction between the amygdala, the hippocampus, and the hypothalamus becomes evident. In the conscious monkey, stimulation of the amygdala leads to a striking rise in plasma 17-hydroxycorticoid levels, and transection of the fornix markedly affects the diurnal fluctuation in the excretion level of the hormone.[43] In a way yet to be fully determined, the endocrine system is thus locked to the great modulator systems which by reciprocal interaction guide the motivational systems in their appropriate response. It is even conceivable that the rhythmic fluctuations in excitability noted above may reflect shifts in balance between systems which figuratively may be referred to as coupled oscillators. Such systems are used with great advantage in the discharge of some simple, autonomic functions in the brain stem, such as the rhythmic discharge of the respiratory center,[44] and would appear to depend upon reciprocal inhibition within a closely knit neural net for their effective operation. There seems little doubt of the operation of reciprocal inhibitory influences within the nets subserving the motivational systems, though it is equally evident that a remarkable modification of this interaction at the hands of modulator systems must have also occurred. By and large, this favors delay in place of immediate discharge; fractioned, graded performance in lieu of display at open throttle. Yet this modulation breaks down under stress. We do not normally laugh and cry at the same time; but we may do so after a catastrophe. We do not normally display the extreme excitement or inordinate muscular power readily observed in an active manic patient or in any one of us when "blinded" by rage. Yet such performance is evidently within the capacity of the ordinary human frame. One should thus not be deceived by appearances, and postulate stimulation wherever one sees overactivity. Stress response may travel in different guises. It may manifest equally as overactivity resulting from the faltering of a physiological braking mechanism, or as underactivity resulting from excessive inhibitory tone, fired, in turn, by a runaway excitatory process. Ideally (though rarely) the balance is neat, and guided by the demands of the "here" and the "now." In stress states, this neat modulation is lost. The balance is more autonomous and more dependent on self-limiting fluctuations. Put another way, the steering mechanisms are set at "automatic."

These three principles, then—the anatomical and cytological suborganization of the systems subserving affective behavior, their interconnectedness, and the balanced, yet mutually occlusive nature of their operation—may give one some indication of the complexities which face a pharmacological approach to this field. This is borne out by several simple, yet telling experiments, of which only three will be cited.

In a study reported in 1957,[45] it could be shown that in rats carrying permanently implanted electrodes in the medial forebrain bundle, near the fornix, dual effects from stimulation via the same electrode could be regularly observed. The animal would press a bar to turn on the stimulation, and thus show an initial reward effect. This, however, would be followed by the turning off of the stimulus (brought about by the turning of a wheel), and presumably signified an escape from "punishing" effects as the stimulus continued. The sequence would be regularly repeated. It was suggested that it reflected a differential rate of recruitment of the patterns of reward and punishment behavior when the systems subserving them were stimulated simultaneously.

It was of interest in these experiments that drugs with effects as opposite as those of methamphetamine (2 mg./kg.) and chlorpromazine (4 mg./kg.) produced roughly similar effects on the overall rate of bar pressing. However, when the positive and negative components were measured separately, striking qualitative differences could be shown. Methamphetamine increased the average time to turn the stimulation off. Chlorpromazine, on the other hand, had its largest effect on the opposite measure; namely, the time the animals waited before the stimulation was turned on. The time to turn the stimulation off was also increased, but much less. Thus, an overall measure (bar pressing) may, in fact, obscure two measures related to different effects possibly exerted on different systems; and do so despite a single electrode placement, which may be mistakenly associated with a single effect.

That such differential effects are likely is brought out by a second series of studies[33] in which the electrode location was varied and the effects of drugs on self-stimulation rates were examined. With electrodes placed in the anterior hypothalamus, self-stimulation rates were little affected by chlorpromazine; but with electrodes in the ventral posterior hypothalamus, there was striking inhibition. There were similar indications of the relation of electrode placement to the effects of other drugs, though the role of stimulus duration and the possibility of biphasic responses should be borne in mind in these experiments. Yet the indications of a preferential effect of some drugs on the appetitive and aversive systems are, at least, suggestive. This is also borne out in yet another study where operant conditioning techniques were employed. It could, for example, be shown in both the rat and the monkey[46] that, whereas pentobarbitone exerted an early effect on avoidance behavior (i.e., reduced the number of responses which, if preserved, prevented the delivery of a shock to the animal), the same drug exerted relatively little effect on appetitive behavior (i.e., while the animal was lever-pressing for a sugar pellet reward). Hyoscine, on the other hand, had the obverse effect: even in small doses, it led to an immediate depressant effect upon reward behavior, while leaving avoidance behavior relatively less affected.

II. SOME ELECTROPHYSIOLOGICAL CORRELATES

Numerous other examples including some early studies[47] could be added to the instances given above. They illustrate the delicate balance between the cell groups governing affective behavior, and the susceptibility to drugs of these actively maintained equilibria. The indicators of shifts in these subsystems in relation to behavior are, at present, few and far between. They are found at the electrophysiological and neurohumoral levels. Some electro-physiological correlates will now be briefly considered.

In inquiries of this kind, particularly when concerned with

similarly, there was also a fall, at much the same rate, in the threshold for arousal by auditory stimulation, while the threshold for single click responses recorded at the cortex remained comparatively unchanged. In doses of 1 mg./kg., there was permanent alerting of the preparation, both in terms of electrical activity and behavior. LSD 25, on the other hand, while exerting (in doses of 1-20 μg./kg.) relatively little effect on arousal to direct stimulation of the reticular formation, caused a marked fall in the threshold for arousal by auditory stimulation. This could be seen in doses of the order of 1-2 μg./kg. Atropine (in doses of 0.2-4 mg./kg.) led to the usual appearance of the characteristic slow wave activity in the electrocorticogram, but left the behavioral threshold (as judged by the criteria enumerated above) relatively unchanged. Although both tactile and auditory stimuli could still produce behavioral alerting after atropine, they did not modify electrical activity. There thus appeared a wide divergence between the threshold for electrocortical arousal and that for arousal in terms of behavioral response.

Physostigmine produced effects opposite to those of atropine, leading to a fall of threshold for electrical activity with relatively little change in behavioral threshold. If injected after atropine (in doses .01-0.8 mg./kg.) this drug would lead to a progressive lowering of the electroencephalographic arousal threshold, as the slow activity induced by atropine gradually gave way to the low voltage fast activity seen with physostigmine. The behavioral threshold, however, was not markedly affected by this drug.

The above parameters were found useful in a subsequent examination of the effects of chlorpromazine and some ten other tranquilizing drugs on the arousal responses in the *encéphale* preparation.[64] Earlier and important[65] experiments, though suggesting an action of chlorpromazine at the level of the reticular activating system, had also emphasized the paradoxical nature of some of these responses. Used in relatively large doses (up to 5 mg./kg.),[65] it could be shown that the drug exerted only slight effects on electroencephalographic and behavioral arousal brought about by stimulation of the reticular formation, while markedly elevating the behavioral arousal threshold to stimulation of the diffuse thalamic projection system. Furthermore, unlike pentobarbital (which diminished conduction time in the reticular formation), chlorpromazine was found to increase reticular input and conduction.[65] Dose, and parameters of stimulation may well be critical in such studies. Thus, for example, in experiments where electrical and behavioral arousal to direct electrical stimulation of the reticular formation were recorded,[64] chlorpromazine in very small doses (0.1-0.5 mg./kg.) caused a slight fall in the behavioral and electrocortical arousal thresholds, in about one third of such experiments. However, with a total dose of 0.8 mg./kg. there was a return to the original threshold. This effect could not be seen with a number of other drugs tested (see below). In the same experiments, doses of 2.0-4 mg./kg. causd a slight rise in threshold for both electrocortical and behavioral arousal. Larger doses caused no further change in threshold.

In contrast to the above relatively slight effects on arousal responses produced by direct stimulation of the reticular formation, the effect of chlorpromazine on arousal responses produced by sensory (auditory) stimulation were quite marked. Small doses (0.1-0.3 mg./kg.) of chlorpromazine produced relatively little effect on these parameters; however, with larger doses (0.5-1.8 mg./kg.) both electrocortical and behavioral thresholds showed a marked rise. Moreover, the arousal responses themselves became less marked, both in terms of extent and duration. In doses of 2.0-4.0 mg./kg. the evoked auditory arousal response was blocked completely. At the same time the preparation became unresponsive to other types of sensory stimulation, although pain (pinching of ears) still produced some response. Interestingly enough, the threshold for single click response recorded at the auditory cortex remained unchanged throughout the experiment.

Since these earlier studies, similar techniques have been applied to an examination of some other drugs.[64] These included promazine, acepromazine, hydroxyzine, benactyzine, imipramine, hyoscine, reserpine, rescinnamine, deserpidine, meprobamate and azacyclonal. According to the responses observed, the drugs

were found to fall into four groups. The results are summarized
in Table I.

TABLE 1. The Effects of Some Drugs on Arousal Thresholds
(AFTER BRADLEY & KEY, 1959.[64])

Group	Principal Characteristics	Drugs Included in Group
I	Slight rise in threshold for arousal through stimulation of the brain stem reticular formation. Marked rise in threshold to arousal to indirect (auditory) stimulation.	Chlorpromazine Promazine Acepromazine Hydroxyzine
II	Marked rise in elecrocortical activation threshold through direct stimulation of brain stem reticular formation; "dissociation" between electrocortical and behavioral arousal.	Benactyzine Imipramine Hyoscine
III	Little effect on arousal thresholds to direct stimulation. "Fast" electrocortical activity in large doses.	Reserpine Rescinnamine Deserpidine
IV	Little effect on arousal thresholds.	Meprobamate Azacyclonal

Group I included drugs which caused only slight diminution
of the arousal responses to direct stimulation of the brain stem
reticular formation, but a rise of threshold to arousal by indirect
sensory (auditory) stimulation. Included in this group are chlorpromazine, promazine, acepromazine and hydroxyzine. It should
be noted that the interaction between these drugs and amphetamine, atropine, and physostigmine was in keeping with previous
findings. Whereas chlorpromazine appeared to block the effects
of amphetamine, the latter drug still produced some effects
when given after promazine, acepromazine and hydroxyzine;
though it never led to complete alerting. Atropine and physostigmine, on the other hand, when superimposed on chlorpromazine,
produced their marked effect on electrical activity of the brain,
but did not modify overt behavior. Most of the drugs in this

group share antiepinephrine properties, though some also show an action against 5-hydroxytryptamine, histamine, and acetylcholine.

Group II. Drugs in this group led to an increase in arousal thresholds, but at the same time produced a dissociation between electrical activity and behavior. Comprised in this group are benactyzine, imipramine, and hyoscine. These drugs did not antagonize the alerting effects of amphetamine on behavior; moreover, they did not markedly affect thresholds for behavioral arousal induced by sensory stimulation. It is well to remember that benactyzine and hyoscine are atropine analogues; and that imipramine, closely allied to promazine, also shares some weak anti-acetylcholine properties. Drugs in this group exert a comparatively weak antiepinephrine action, and appear more effective in blocking the blood pressure and antispasmodic effects of acetylcholine than do drugs in the other groups.

Group III. This group comprises drugs which have relatively little effect on arousal thresholds, but which, in full doses, cause marked changes in the electrocorticogram towards the "activation" pattern. Included in this group are reserpine and two related compounds, rescinnamine and deserpidine. These drugs produced no change in the threshold for arousal by stimulation of the brain stem, although they did, in large doses, lead to a change in the electrocorticogram towards a faster frequency. This, however, appeared unrelated to the behavioral state, the preparation usually showing little evidence of arousal. Drugs in this group, although possessing some antispasmodic activity against epinephrine, acetylcholine, and histamine, share a depleting action on the stores of serotonin and of catecholamines in the brain (see below).

Group IV. Drugs in this group could not be shown to exert any marked effect either on electrocortical activity or on the behavioral arousal threshold. Included in this group are meprobamate and azacyclonal. Meprobamate (in doses of 20-40 mg./kg.) had no effect on thresholds of arousal induced by direct stimulation of the reticular formation. Equally, the responses to afferent stimulation showed little change, and even with large doses, the electrocorticogram remained relatively unaltered. Somewhat similar effects were observed with azacyclonal.

The above studies give an indication of the broad and empirically crude nature of any grouping so far possible on the basis of neurophysiological evidence. It is obvious that the electrophysiological effects of the diverse tranquilizers are not necessarily related to their clinical effectiveness, and that they can at best give only a very inadequate indication as to their mode of action. This is borne out by two further sets of observations not unrelated to the above studies; these concern so-called stimulating (rather than tranquilizing) agents.

It has been suggested that dimethylaminoethanol (DMAE) owes its central stimulant effects to a possible role as a precursor of acetylcholine within the central nervous system.[66] In a recent study the effects of this drug, and of amphetamine have been compared.[67] DMAE was indeed found to lower the threshold for electroencephalographic arousal elicited both by stimulation of the reticular formation and also following thalamic stimulation. The increased activity of the latter was found to be insufficient to increase the low-voltage fast electroencephalographic activity in the absence of acsending influences from the reticular formation. DMAE was thus presumed to have a tonic effect on the entire reticular formation. The compound was found to antagonize the depressant effects of barbiturates on the pathways subserving wakefulness. The action of DMAE on the reticular activating system was thus similar to, but not as striking as that of amphetamine.

Another study[68,69] has compared the effects of drugs used in the treatment of depression in terms of their effect on electrocortical (though not behavioral) arousal. The drugs were found to fall into two groups. The first, which included amphetamine, pipradrol, methylphenidate, iproniazid, and DMAE, was found to lead to electrocortical "arousal." The second group did not share this property, and was thought to block the mesodiencephalic arousal system (MDAS). Inasmuch as this group included benactyzine and imipramine it presumably corresponded to Group II in the series previously cited.

The equivocal position of the last two drugs should, incidentally, be noted. Benactyzine, which started as a minor tranquilizer,[70] can also, apparently, be viewed as a stimulant; and imipramine, though an antidepressant, is closely related to promazine, a tranquilizer.[71]

Viewed in terms of possible modes of action, amphetamine and chlorpromazine have some slight advantage over the other drugs so far considered. In the case of both, there is some circumstantial evidence for the involvement of a catechol amine mediated mechanism. The evidence for a possible central adrenergic mechanism in the action of amphetamine has been briefly referred to above. The obverse, in a sense, appears to be true for chlorpromazine and allied drugs, where a central antiepinephrine effect is not out of keeping with the evidence. These drugs would appear to act less by a direct depression of the arousal mechanism than by an effect on an element or mechanism intermediate between afferent input and the arousal mechanism, or on tonic inhibitory influences playing upon the reticular core from high subcortical cell masses. The relatively slight effect on arousal thresholds to direct stimulation; the marked effect on threshold to arousal by indirect sensory (auditory) stimulation; the marked antagonism to amphetamine, and the antiepinephrine properties of this group of drugs would suggest an interference with a central adrenergic process which in some way regulates the balance of inhibitory tone governing conduction within the reticular formation. Two other curious findings concerning chlorpromazine may be quoted. The first is the slight fall of threshold brought about by small doses.[64] The second is the increase in conduction time following chlorpromazine.[65] The shifts within the system are thus subtle and dose dependent; and a change in response to afferent stimulation (as reflected in the discrepancy between the responses to direct and indirect stimulation) may in some manner reflect an increased capacity of the reticular core to "filter"[65] sensory input without necessarily engaging the reticular-hypothalamic mechanisms. One must surmise that the catecholamines may play a part in maintaining the balance between excitation and inhibition in key areas of the reticular system, which, indeed is a system of systems.

Unit Activity in the Reticular Formation as Studied by Microelectrode Techniques

There is a further kind of experiment which can be used to study interaction at the level here considered. The microelectrode studies of spontaneous and evoked activity of units in the reticular formation[72] invite an extension of such studies into the pharmacological field. In one such preliminary study[73,74] recordings were obtained from single units in the mesencephalon and medulla, using floating microelectrodes. Blood pressure was recorded simultaneously to control for vasomotor effects. The units selected for observation were classified as reticular in character from the fact that they showed convergence responses, and from the effects observed by stimulation through microelectrodes after recordings had been completed. Observations were also made on a number of units belonging to specific sensory projection systems, such as for example units situated in the mesencephalic nucleus of the fifth nerve, or the superior colliculus. The drugs were administered by the intravenous or intracarotid route.

The studies concerned primarily the effects of epinephrine, acetylcholine, and chlorpromazine, and it is for this reason that they are mentioned in the present context. With epinephrine variable effects were observed. The activity of units was either unaffected, or showed an increase or a decrease in the rate of discharge. Following intravenous injection, the effects were usually seen only during a rise in blood pressure; but following intracarotid injections (of 1-5 μg.) the effects were similar, though no change in blood pressure could be observed. The effects of acetylcholine (which was applied in doses of 0.2-1.0 μg. by the intracarotid route only) were somewhat different. These responses were of two kinds: first, a primary increase or decrease in frequency, starting within a few seconds of the injection and lasting only a few seconds; second, a response of much longer latency. The latter appeared more constant and was observed in every unit tested; whereas the primary effect was not always seen. The secondary effect was invariably accompanied by a slight fall in blood pressure, though no change in blood pressure was observed during the primary effect. These effects were still present after bilateral denervation of the carotid sinus and also following the injection of a paralyzing dose of tubocurarine. These units, therefore, were capable of being either facilitated or inhibited following the intracarotid administration of these drugs. It was of interest, also, that units belonging to the specific sensory systems of the brain stem were not affected by the injections of epinephrine. This striking difference in susceptibility, which is in keeping with more recent findings in other specific sensory systems,[75] may well be of significance to a theory of the interaction-in-time of the specific and the nonspecific projection systems.

Chlorpromazine, when applied in doses of 2 to 4 mg./kg., led to a marked decrease in the frequency of the spontaneous activity of units; moreover, the units became much less responsive to peripheral stimuli. Thus, "a unit which previously responded to light stabbing or stroking of one of the legs with a burst of 9 to 10 spikes consistently produced only 2 or 3 spikes in response to a similar stimulus after chlorpromazine had been injected."[73] This effect was observed to occur with doses of 2 to 4 mg./kg. intravenously (a dose which, as noted above, is effective in blocking arousal to afferent stimulation). Further increase in this dose did not increase the effect, and even with the largest doses some response to tapping of the legs was always obtained. If pentobarbitone or sodium pentothal was administered after chlorpromazine, all spontaneous activity disappeared and no responses from the unit could be obtained. The activity reappeared within twenty or thirty minutes after injection, and eventually recovered fully when the effect of the barbiturates had worn off. The effect was not observed with barbiturates alone. It suggested a synergism between chlorpromazine and barbiturates.

III. SOME NEUROHUMORAL CORRELATES

The above instances have been chosen to illustrate the hybrid nature of the type of compound dealt with so far, which cuts through much that is tacitly implicit in the older concepts of stimulation and depression. As in the case of morphia, behavioral and affective under-responsiveness may well be an active state. It is at present impossible, nor is it conceptually permissible, to locate the action of the psycho-active drugs to any particular area or any particular cell group. All one can assume is a shift within the balancing processes which normally regulate the interaction-in-time between widely scattered neural nets converging in several nodal areas. The interconnectedness of the various subsystems concerned with affective response has already been emphasized. Fibre length and thickness, precise dendritic arrangement and synaptic delay will determine the timing and coincidence of patterns in these widely separated cell lattices. Yet, assuming that certain standard processes determine the primary synaptic events within such vast cell assemblies, we have still to account, somehow, in chemical terms for the altered thresholds which lead to the selective suppression or release, the gating, in terms of storage or flow, of the highly organized patterns of activity which we know as affective behavior. It has been suggested[53] that the regulation of levels of excitability in such neural nets may involve the interaction of humoral field effects and highly localized synaptic events in certain trigger areas of the brain stem. Cholinergic as well as noncholinergic elements may be involved in this interaction. The regional and local economy, in terms of neurohumoral mediation, may therefore be relevant to the action of the drugs discussed so far. Some of these neurohumoral correlates will now be considered.

A rich literature has grown around the subject of central synaptic transmission, and only a few aspects will be mentioned within the present context. It may be useful to begin by agreeing on four minimal desiderata[52] which should be fulfilled by a substance claiming the role of a neurohumoral mediator within the central nervous system. First, the substance should be present in the central nervous system and should vary in concentration with the functional state of the tissue. Second, enzyme systems (both for the synthesis and for the destruction of the substance in question) should be present in the areas of the central nervous system where the substance is normally found. Third, these enzymes should be susceptible to inhibition by specific inhibitors or antimetabolites and the effects of such inhibition should be clearly demonstrable in chemical or functional terms. Fourth, the application of the hypothetical agent or its precursor to the central nervous system, either directly or by a physiological route, should exert clear effects on function.

These criteria are met in part by a number of substances, though, significantly, in the case of each, important reservations obtain. Thus, for example, though acetylcholine is present in the central nervous system, the enzyme system concerned in its synthesis (the choline acetylase system) has a curiously uneven distribution, some areas of the central nervous system being strikingly low in the enzyme.[76] The central role of acetylcholine, and related choline esters has been more fully considered elsewhere.[52,53,77] Recent attention has been directed towards substances other than acetylcholine; these include epinephrine, *nor*epinephrine, and related catechol amines; serotonin, and a group of related indoles; and, surprisingly, a number of amino acids which have been found capable of markedly affecting synaptic transmission.

Norepinephrine, Epinephrine, Serotonin and Related Substances

It has been shown that *nor*epinephrine (with an admixture of 5-20% epinephrine) has a differential pattern of distribution within the brain.[59] This pattern is different from that of acetylcholine. The highest concentrations of *nor*epinephrine are found in the hypothalamus, the area postrema, and the periventricular grey substance; other parts of the mesencephalon and the medulla also contain sizeable concentrations. A third catecholamine, dopamine (a probable precursor of epinephrine), has also been shown to be present in the brain; though, significantly, its distribution is different from that of *nor*epinephrine, the highest concentration being found in the lentiform and the caudate nucleus.[78,79]

The tissue catecholamines appear to be associated with particulate cell constituents, microsome-like granules rich in

ATP.[80,81] The synthesis of catecholamine proceeds by way of several distinct steps. The parent substance is the amino acid, tyrosine, from which 3, 4-dihydroxyphenylalanine (DOPA) is formed by oxidation. DOPA is changed to dopamine by the action of an enzyme, dopa decarboxylase, in the presence of pyridoxal phosphate, which acts as a coenzyme. This enzyme has been identified both in the sympathetic ganglia and in the grey matter of the central nervous system[82]; though, to date, its regional distribution is relatively unknown. The subsequent step of oxidation of dopamine to *nor*epinephrine has been demonstrated by the use of isotopically labeled precursors *in vivo*,[83] and in perfusion experiments.[84] The nature and the catalysts involved in this reaction are relatively unknown at present. The final step is the N-methylation of *nor*epinephrine to epinephrine. It is likely that adenosyl methionine acts as a methyl donor in this reaction.[85]

Two points are worthy of note in regard to the possible synthesis of the substance in the brain. It has been shown that isotopically (tritium) labeled epinephrine does not readily cross the blood-brain barrier, except possibly in small amounts in the region of the hypothalamus[86]; on the other hand, dopa, its precursor, can readily enter the central nervous system and can be shown to exert marked central effects.[79] Moreover, the intravenous injection of dopa in rabbits can cause large increases in the concentration of dopamine in the brain, whereas the levels of *nor*epinephrine and epinephrine may not be significantly changed.[87] However, after catecholamine depletion by reserpine, dopa restores catecholamine levels within a matter of hours. This strongly suggests that the brain possesses the enzymes necessary for the synthesis of catecholamines from its precursors.

The inactivation of epinephrine by way of O-methylation through catechol O-methyl-transferase, an enzyme present in the brain, has been considered in detail in the preceding paper.[88] The speed of the reaction should be noted. The disposition of the methylated metabolite is carried forward further by mono amine oxidase to 3-methoxy-4-hydroxy mandelic acid (vanillyl mandelic acid, VMA).[89] Although it is highly probable that the catecholamines are, for the greater part, O-methylated before they are oxidized, it is also possible that some oxidation may precede O-methylation to a limited extent. In this context, however, the relative slowness of the reaction of mono-amine oxidase with epinephrine is of interest. Both the precursor (dopamine) and the methylated product (metanephrine or *nor*metanephrine) would appear to form better substrates for the action of this enzyme than does epinephrine itself. Though a direct protective action of mono-amine oxidase inhibitors, such as iproniazid and beta phenylisopropylhydrazine (JB-516), on *nor*epinephrine and epinephrine cannot be excluded, it is at least equally likely that the action may be exerted by increasing the stores of dopamine and thus, possibly, the source material for *nor*epinephrine. Be this as it may, *nor*epinephrine, epinephrine, and their precursor, dopamine, have been definitely identified in the central nervous system. The brain apparently possesses the enzymes for both the manufacture and the disposal of these powerful amines. Equally, there is suggestive evidence, mentioned above and reviewed elsewhere[90] for a central action of these substances.

The third agent implicated in the central action of psychotropic drugs is 5-hydroxytryptamine (serotonin). Its occurrence in the brain was demonstrated quite early,[91] and its distribution parallels that of *nor*epinephrine, the highest yields being obtained in the hypothalamus, the area postrema, and the periventricular grey.[92,93] However, high values are also found in the amygdala, thalamus and certain areas of the limbic system,[93] such as the hippocampal gyrus, orbital gyrus, the cingulate and retrosplenial cortex, the septal nuclei, and the habenula.

Serotonin is derived from the amino acid tryptophan, from which its immediate precursor 5-hydroxytryptophan is formed by oxidation. The conversion of 5-hydroxytrytophan into serotonin is brought about by way of decarboxylation. The enzyme concerned, 5-hydroxytryptophan decarboxylase, has been shown to have a distribution similar to serotonin,[94] and in its requirement for pyridoxal phosphate as coenzyme, and in its distribution in the cytoplasmic fraction of brain homogenate, closely resembles dopa decarboxylase. There is a further similarity between the catecholamine systems and the system here considered. For, though serotonin itself does not appear to transfer readily through the blood brain barrier, as evidenced by the lack of accumulation of serotonin in the brain following infusion and the lack, for example, of central symptoms in carcinoid tumors, the administration of 5-hydroxytryptophan increases brain 5HT levels significantly and leads to marked central effects.[95] Here again, there is thus indirect evidence of the local manufacture of serotonin from its immediate precursor, though it must remain undetermined what proportion of these effects may be due to the immediate effect of 5-hydroxytrypto-phan, or to 5-hydroxytryptamine.

Unlike epinephrine and *nor*epinephrine, however, there would appear to be good reason for believing that mono-amine oxidase may be responsible for the disposition of serotonin in the central nervous system. Inhibition of amine oxidase by iproniazid leads to an increase of brain serotonin level.[95,96] The product of deamination (5-hydroxy-indole acetic acid, 5HIAA) is the main urinary metabolite of serotonin; after inhibition of amine oxidase there is sharp fall of 5-hydroxy-indole acetic acid.[97,98] In fact, this fall of 5HIAA excretion can be used as a guide in evaluating the efficiency of an amine oxidase inhibitor in man.[98] Furthermore, in the presence of an amine oxidase inhibitor (for example, iproniazid, or JB-516), the injection of 5-hydroxytryptophan leads to a marked rise in brain serotonin. Amine oxidase inhibitors can also be used to study the turnover of serotonin in the brain. Preliminary experiments suggest this to be high.[99] Thus, in the case of serotonin, (as in the case of epinephrine) the principal criteria appear to be met; though the precise effects of administration differ considerably according to where, how, and how much of the substance is applied at any particular time.

The Synaptically Active Amino Acids

There is a fourth group of substances which has recently been shown to exert an effect on synaptic transmission within the central nervous system. This includes a series of amino acids, such as the ω-guanidino acids and, to a lesser extent, the α-guanidino acids,[100] but is best represented in the striking distribution and effects of γ-amino butyric acid (GABA[101,102,103]). This substance is found in readily extractable form in large quantities in the central nervous system of a number of species. It is formed from glutamic acid by the action of glutamic acid decarboxylase (GAD). Both GABA itself and the decarboxylase are found in higher yield in gray than in white matter, and both are laid down very rapidly in the brain during early postnatal development. The decarboxylation of glutamic acid to γ-amino-butyrate requires the presence of pyridoxal phosphate, and thus brings the formation of this acid into intimate relationship with cellular oxidation.

The disposition of GABA is carried through by GABA trans-aminase (GABA-T), an enzyme found in the brain and other tissues, which brings about the transamination of GABA with α-ketoglutarate to form l-glutamic acid and succinic semialdehyde. The latter compound is then oxidized to succinic acid in the brain, the succinate entering the tricarboxylic cycle. The distribution of GABA-T and GAD in the nervous system of the monkey is uneven.[104,105] The relatively high concentration of GABA-T, *inter alia*, in the hypothalamus and the olivary nucleus is noteworthy.

As is the case with *nor*epinephrine and serotonin, GABA itself does not readily penetrate the blood brain barrier, but depends for its presence in the brain on local manufacture from its precursor, glutamic acid. A number of other findings should also be noted. The enzymes concerned with the synthesis (GAD) and the disposition (GABA-T) of GABA show a remarkable sensitivity to pH, GAD showing maximal activity at pH6.5, and GABA-T at pH8.2.[103] Small shifts in intracellular pH (occasioned for example by CO_2 shifts and differences in the activity of carbonic anhydrase) could thus be envisioned to affect profoundly the levels of intracellular GABA. The amount of GABA present in any particular area must thus reflect a balance between the rate of formation and the rate of utilization of the material; and the level of enzyme activity in a particular area (and the ratio between the activity of the two enzymes) may thus be a much more accurate indicator of GABA activity in a particular area than is the actual amount of GABA present at a particular time. Fortunately, the activity of these enzymes can be affected. The semicarbazides, by interfering with pyridoxal phosphate activity (an essential coenzyme factor in the action of the decarboxylase) can inhibit decarboxylase activity, leading to a fall in GABA levels in the central nervous system. Hydroxylamine, on the other hand, can be shown to inhibit GABA-transferase (GABA-T) more than the decarboxylase, and thus leads to an endogenous accumulation of GABA *in vivo*.[106]

The first indication of a possible physiological role of GABA in the mammalian nervous system stems from the demonstration of the convulsive properties of the semicarbazides,[107] the application of which *in vivo* was found to lead to repetitive seizures following a significantly long latent period. This presumably resulted from the fall in endogenously produced GABA, and was borne out by the fact that the topical application of low doses of GABA reduced or blocked electrically induced seizures in the hippocampus.[108] Hydroxylamine, on the other hand, led to a marked reduction in the duration and spread of electrically induced after-discharges in the cat in acute experiments, and in conscious monkeys carrying in-dwelling electrodes.[109] The monkeys appeared more placid without being sedated, and were much easier to handle for as long as seven hours after the administration of hydroxylamine.[109] The predominantly inhibitory role of GABA on synaptic transmission has been stressed in a number of studies,[110] though its universal role as a principal inhibitory substance in the mammalian central nervous system can by no means be regarded as settled.[111]

The above findings are mentioned because they represent a significant break in a tradition which, up to quite recently, has unduly emphasized a distinction between the power economy, the protein synthesis, and the processes and agents affecting the electrogenic properties, and the permeability, of the neurone membrane. Distinctions such as these are no doubt convenient, and can be readily made in the mind; they help to delimit one's problem and to guide one's experiment. They are, however, unlikely to be made in the cell, where the various phases appear functionally linked and interdependent. Thus, for example, the rate of protein synthesis in the brain, and the rate of turnover of amino acids is known to be very high.[112] Glutamic acid (the parent substance of GABA) has been long known to play a part in energy metabolism and protein synthesis.[113] Yet its derivative, GABA, together with other amino acids, can be shown to exert effects on synaptic transmission which, to say the least, are quite respectable. One must thus assume that if, indeed, such substances do naturally occur in the central nervous system, their effect must be both local and transient; and that some subcellular compartmentalization[114] carefully regulates the manufacture, storage, release, and inactivation of the various agents, quite possibly in different proportions and at different rates. One is also struck by certain common features shared by the agents considered so far. In the case of each (acetylcholine, *nor*epinephrine, serotonin and GABA), the active agent, though readily formed in the brain, does not readily penetrate the blood brain barrier; their precursors (dopa, 5-hydroxytryptophan, glutamic acid) do so fairly readily, and are found in some instances (such as in the case of dopamine) to have a distribution pattern rather different from their products. Again, the enzyme systems for their synthesis and disposition have a differential distribution pattern throughout the brain; and though sharing certain features in common (for example dependence upon decarboxylation in the case of dopamine, 5-hydroxytryptophan and glutamic acid), also show marked differences in respect to other enzyme activity (for example, their differential susceptibility to mono-amine oxidase, or O-methyltransferase). Furthermore, there is some suggestive evidence of susceptibility in some cases, to strictly local conditions (for example, local pH in the case of GAD and GABA-T). The picture which thus emerges is one of convergence and interaction between a number of highly localized processes, proceeding at different rates and, possibly, at different subcellular sites in the same segment of time. Their coincidence and relative overlap may profoundly determine the final sequence of events leading to discharge in a particular cell assembly.

Some Interactions Between Drugs and Neuroeffector Substances Within the Central Nervous System

The interrelatedness and the importance of relative and local shifts within a relatively small area is borne out by the complex and multiple effects of drugs on levels of neuroeffector substances within the nervous system. This can be observed at both central and peripheral sites. In a series of early experiments, it was shown that depletion of hypothalamic catecholamines could be brought about by a variety of drugs, some of which were convulsants (such as caffeine, leptazol, nicotine, and picrotoxin) and some which were accounted as behaviorally depressant (such as morphine).[59] There was excellent correlation between the loss of hypothalamic *nor*epinephrine and adrenal medullary *nor*epinephrine. Furthermore, there was a correlation between loss of *nor*epinephrine in the hypothalamus and in the midbrain. These experiments suggested that depletion of hypothalamic *nor*epinephrine was related to the stimulation of the sympathetic center of the brain stem; though it should be noted in passing that both stimulants and depressants were apparently capable of inducing such chemically judged stimulation; and that, though morphine had a depleting effect on hypothalamic catecholamine levels, this property was shared by such diverse agents as insulin, and ether.[115]

The situation was found to be somewhat different in the case of reserpine. This drug leads to a release of large amounts of serotonin from body depots, and strikingly lowers brain 5-HT levels within four hours of administration. These effects may persist for several days.[116,117] During this period of low serotonin levels, the excretion of 5-hydroxy-indole acetic acid also rises. This suggests that, in the reserpinized animal, serotonin continues to be formed at a normal rate; but that there is an inability on the part of the tissues to bind the substance, with a consequent vulnerability of serotonin to oxidation by mono-amine oxidase. The inhibition of mono-amine oxidase by iproniazid prior to the administration of reserpine converts the sedative action of reserpine to a stimulant one,[117,118,119] there being, on the face of it, a beguilingly direct correlation between a lowering of brain serotonin levels and the sedative action of reserpine.

The complexity of the matter, however, is illustrated by a number of further observations. First, reserpine not only depletes serotonin, but also lowers the levels of *nor*epinephrine in the brain,[120] a property which it shares with a number of drugs already mentioned. Secondly, dopamine (a precursor of epinephrine) also disappears from the brain following treatment with reserpine.[87,121] Thirdly, when considered quantitatively there is, in contrast to other catecholamine depleting drugs, no parallelism in the case of reserpine between the central sympathetic activities (as judged by adrenal medullary catecholamine depletion) and the loss of catecholamines from the brain.[115,120] Lastly, the striking reduction of brain catecholamines by reserpine does not (in keeping with the above findings) result in a reduction of the electrical activity of the sympathetic outflow of the preganglionic fibres,[115] despite the marked reduction of the excitability of post-ganglionic fibres in the sympathetic chain. This would rather lead one to believe that a low residue of catecholamines or serotonin is not necessarily related to a loss of central sympathetic activity. Furthermore, it was found that animals sedated by reserpine could be aroused by a number of drugs, such as morphia, amphetamine, and LSD-25.[115]

Discrepancies such as these suggest that one may be dealing with rather local and relative shifts, possibly at intracellular level. Some recent experiments are in keeping with this view.

In these studies,[87,121] the intracellular distribution of epinephrine, *nor*epinephrine, and hydroxytyramine (dopamine) was examined in terms of partition between mitochondria and cytoplasm of the substances concerned. The brain stem of the rabbit was used. The normal distribution was compared with that following reserpine, and the effect of administration of dopa was also studied. It was found that in the untreated animal, epinephrine, *nor*epinephrine, and hydroxytyramine (dopamine) were present in the ratio of 1: 4: 5, and that each was distributed approximately evenly between the particulate fraction (consisting mainly of mitochondria) and the cytoplasm. Reserpine was used in doses which brought about the disappearance of approximately 50% of the catecholamines within four hours; it was found that the rate of disappearance for all three amines was similar. However, the cytoplasmic fraction was depleted more rapidly than the particulate fraction, and this depletion was maintained irrespective of whether the amine oxidase had been inhibited by prior injection of iproniazid. The intravenous injection of dopa in the reserpinized animal was found to restore the concentration of epinephrine and *nor*epinephrine to normal levels within an hour. Interestingly enough, the level of hydroxytyramine (dopamine) was increased far beyond the control level. The concentration of all amines was raised in both cellular fractions, suggesting that reserpine did not prevent the uptake of amines by the particulate components. The effect of dopa on brain catecholamines in untreated animals was similar. It, too, caused a striking rise in hydroxytyramine, though epinephrine and *nor*epinephrine were not significantly raised above their normal level. This suggested that the brain stem tissue was capable of rapid synthesis of epinephrine, provided dopa was supplied; and that normal concentrations were close to saturation level. The above study did not examine the effect of similar procedures on the intracellular distribution of serotonin, which, presumably (because of its greater susceptibility to mono-amine oxidase) might have shown a rather different pattern. However, there is now some evidence that following reserpine, serotonin, in contrast to the catecholamines, disappears more rapidly from the particulate than the soluble fraction.[122] This would not be out of keeping with the original suggestion that the action of reserpine depends on free serotonin.

Many more facts could be added to the ones already cited. They would, however, merely confuse an already tangled issue, and by their own accumulation point to the urgency of inquiries of a rather different kind. It is regrettable that though many excellent studies have centered on single substances and single neurohumoral systems, very few studies have considered the effects of graded doses of the same drugs on the *relative* concentration of suspected key substances and their associated enzyme systems in discrete areas of the brain, or have weighed the possible *inter*action between substances in relation to chemically induced behavioral states or chemically induced electrophysiological change. Yet, it is submitted that it is the *relative* ratio of one substance to another — the ratio of, say a choline ester, a catecholamine, or an indole amine, or GABA in a particular place at a particular time—which may profoundly affect the net effect at a particular site. *Change* in concentration would thus seem to matter as much as absolute amount, and rate of reaction may be at least as important as the kind of reaction one is considering. It is, in fact, the relative interaction between reactions proceeding at rather different rates, which may affect the anchoring or release of a particular substance from its binding site, and thus modulate the opening or closure of the switchgear at some of the nodal points in the brain considered above.

That such relative shifts in concentration may, in fact, decisively influence the physiological effects of neuroeffector agents is illustrated by a second, and much older, set of experiments,[123,124,125,126] which has been quoted previously in a cognate discussion.[127] In 1941 it was shown that even small amounts of epinephrine, applied in experiments which allowed for separate perfusion of the spinal cord, could markedly affect the response to a given dose of acetylcholine, applied to the perfusate. Small doses of epinephrine steadied the muscle responses to acetylcholine; large doses (of the order of 100 μg) increased the (knee jerk) reflex, and very large doses (of the order of 300 μg.) led to a prolonged diminution.[126] In somewhat similar experiments, carried on a few years later, the interaction between acetylcholine and epinephrine was examined in the superior cervical ganglion preparation.[124,125] In both situations the balance of evidence suggested that whereas epinephrine had relatively little effect by itself, it was capable of profoundly modifying the response to acetylcholine. Small doses usually led to facilitation; larger doses, to inhibition. It was of interest, also, that in observing the effect of these agents on spinal movement patterns in the decerebrate preparation[128] the effects of epinephrine on flexors appeared opposite to its effects on extensors, and usually opposed those of acetylcholine. Though the variety of responses elicited in this particular series was inordinately wide, one cannot but again be struck by the reality of interaction between these two agents, and the wide repertoire of responses elicitable by this interaction. It would appear that epinephrine can modulate responses to acetylcholine,[129] and that the net resultant of this interaction depends upon the relative proportions of the two substances, at particular sites at a particular time.

Possible Hormonal Factors Affecting Binding and Release of Neuroeffector Agents

The above examples are cited merely to indicate the kind of subcellular level of organization which seems to be the business level of the shifts and transactions so far considered. Little is known of the physiological (rather than pharmacological) factors which govern the storage and release of substances at these subcellular sites. One would naturally suspect ionic shifts, though the evidence in this respect, so far, is very circumstantial. Equally, the role of hormones in these transactions is, at present, hardly more than suggestive.

There is a respectable body of evidence, recently admirably reviewed,[130] which indicates a close physiological interaction between the cortical steroids and the epinephrines. The two groups of hormones would seem to operate physiologically as one functional unit. The steroids maintain the integrity and responsiveness of tissues in the process of reacting to the epinephrines; many actions of the epinephrines are not elicitable in the absence of steroids. Equally, and perhaps more significantly, however, many actions attributed to the steroids may, in fact, be more cogently ascribed to the action of the epinephrines.[130] It is therefore of particular interest that there are at present some early indications of the effects of hormones on levels of neuroeffector substances in the brain. Adrenalectomy leads to an increase of brain serotonin.[131] Exposure of rats to stress both of a cold (0° C) and of a warm (37° C) environment prevents the release of serotonin by reserpine; it also prevents sedation

by this substance.[132] Also, a more recent series has shown a marked
depletion of *nor*epinephrine (though not of serotonin) after
exposure of rats to cold stress.[133] A differential response of this
kind is of interest, and may point to an as yet totally unexplored
dependence of drug effects on hormonal equilibria within the
brain itself. It would indeed be well to explore systematically
the effect of graded hormone concentrations both on drug
responsiveness and on the effects of drugs on the binding of
amines at their unknown subcellular anchoring sites. This problem
can perhaps be approached at a local as well as a systemic
level. It can, for example, be shown that very small stereotactically
placed implants of a hormone (stilbestrol dibutyrate) in the
posterior hypothalamus will release a stereotyped form of behavior
(sexual behavior) in the cat.[134] The effect shows some specificity
for both the hormone and the placement of the hormone. Little
is at present known of the precise neural mechanism governing
this release of a behavioral pattern. Earlier studies,[135] however,
would make one suspect a participation of neuroeffector substances in the ultimate mediation of a pituitary response, and it is
conceivable that in the above experiments also, a local interaction
between the hormone and elements in the immediate vicinity of
the implant may lead to significant changes in the balance of
neuroeffector substances at a regional level.

The scanty clinical data so far available on the relation of plasma
hydrocortisone level to affect give further pause for thought.
There is a significant and linear relationship between an increase
in anxiety, anger, and plasma hydrocortisone levels.[136] Moreover,
and perhaps less expected, it has been shown that severe depression
is also accompanied by elevated plasma hydrocortisone levels,[137]
and that deeply retarded and underactive patients show hormone
levels higher than those in a less depressed group. Depression would
thus appear to be an active stress response; and the retarded, tear-
less state a final phase in an active, adaptive process. This phase
is largely inhibitory, as against the excitatory components commonly seen in the so-called "agitated depressive syndromes." It
would be idle to speculate at present as to the possible effect of
these various degrees of pituitary-adrenocortical mobilization on

the binding and release of neuroeffector substances in nodal (or trigger) areas of the brain. It may even be that the reverse is true, and that differential proportions of catecholamines within the brain may affect the degree of adrenocortical mobilization. Yet there is some evidence, quoted in an adjoining paper,[138] for the influence of purely situational factors on the relative proportions of *nor*epinephrine and epinephrine in the plasma. Lability or over-activity or underactivity may, however, have its neurohumoral correlates in the brain, as well as in the plasma. The data to date are scanty. Many more are needed before a rational hypothesis to account for these various states can be put forward.

IV. TOWARDS AN ANALYSIS OF REGIONAL PROCESS WITHIN THE BRAIN

The above findings and many others, of necessity omitted, serve to emphasize the importance of regional and local economy in the function of the brain as a detector and organizer of spatiotem-poral change in the course of adaptive behavior. The anatomical and cytological suborganization of even quite small areas of the brain has been mentioned; it is reflected by sharp regional differ-ences in chemical constitution at cellular and, quite possibly, sub-cellular[139] levels. Nor would it be appropriate to assume that local and, in some areas, rather specific chemical properties are not reflected in differences in local permeability of the blood brain barrier or in strictly local changes in small vessel tone. There are, in fact, early indications that the converse may be true; that some areas (for example, the hypothalamus) may be differentially per-meable to some metabolites,[86] and that change in local function may be related to change in local blood flow.[140] The principle of shielding, and of metabolic autonomy, so strikingly reflected in the existence of the blood brain barrier, may well have deeper meaning, and have to be carried into the chemical architecture of the brain itself. For all one knows, there may be pericellular barriers in some areas (for example the so-called "specific" lateral pathways); and local vascular shunts may well meet varying local needs. It may no longer be sufficient to look for differences in enzyme constitution between gross cell masses to account for a differential susceptibility of the nervous system to neuroleptic agents. Such differences must be sought at a more discrete level. As no other organ in the body, the brain has evolved as an aggregate of suborgans, resulting in—if one may so put it—an assembly of chemically mediated homeostats. The chemical imprints of this evolution are becoming evident with time. A principle of metabolic compartmentalization[141] is emerging, of which the highly localized synthesis, storage, release, and disposition of neuroeffector substances at subcellular sites is but one instance. The convergence, relative ratio, and turnover-in-time of a few relatively simple interlocking chemical reactions may profoundly affect excitability thresholds at particular sites at a particular time. The nodal midline areas appear to be peculiarly susceptible to such chemical shifts. Only overall data are so far available of the nature of these shifts; they do, however, suggest some similarity with mechanisms employed in neurohumoral mediation elsewhere.

It has been felt by the writer for some time[127,142,51,52,53] that these and cognate interactions may depend upon the presence and uneven distribution in the central nervous system of small families of compounds, derived from neuroeffector substances long familiar for their peripheral effects, yet possessed of special properties in the central nervous system, not shared in peripheral autonomic nets. Acetylcholine, epinephrine and serotonin may be prototypes of this kind. But behind acetylcholine there now stand esters other than acetylcholine; behind epinephrine there is hydroxytyramine; and behind serotonin melanotonin.[143] Hypotheses linked solely to one or other of these agents have not stood the test of time. It is upon distribution gradients of these and cognate substances that some of the modulating and gating mechanisms in the central nervous system may well depend.

It is therefore encouraging that methods for the analysis of regional transactions within the brain are now becoming available. The quantitative histochemistry of some enzyme systems in relation to cell population is feasible,[144,145,146,147] and is bound sooner or later to be related to the action of drugs[148] at subcellular sites. Equally, the effects of drugs[149] and of hormones[134] applied to discrete areas of the brain are now being studied in relation to behavior; and though the interpretation of such effects is an admittedly hazardous undertaking, it is bound to become more discrete and precise with growing experience of the field. Furthermore, the electro-physiological correlates of such procedures are bound to be explored, and to be increasingly related to the electro-physiological correlates of conditioning, viewed in terms of the coding and transformation of signals within the brain.[150] The shadows of which Maudsley spoke are thus sharpening into silhouettes; and in this process of growing understanding, the drugs influencing affect and behavior may play a part far beyond their empirical yield.

REFERENCES

1. Maudsley, Henry: *The Physiology and Pathology of the Mind,* Third Edition, Part 2. New York, D. Appleton & Co., 1882, p. 195.

2. Kety, S. S., Editor: The Pharmacology of Psychotomimetic and Psychotherapeutic Drugs. *Ann. New York Acad. Sc. 66 (3):* 417, 1957.

3. Wikler, A.: *The Relation of Psychiatry to Pharmacology.* Baltimore, Williams & Wilkins, 1957.

4. Cole, J. O., and Gerard, R. W., Editors: *Psychopharmacology Problems in Evaluation; Proc. Conf. on the Evaluation of Pharmacotherapy in Mental Illness, Washington, D. C., 1956.* Washington, D. C., Nat. Acad. Sc. Nat. Res. Council Pub. 583, 1959.

5. Kline, N. S., Editor: *Psychopharmacology Frontiers: Proc. of Psychopharmacology Symposium, Internat. Congr. of Psychiatry, 2d, Zürich, 1957,* Boston, Little, Brown & Co., 1959.

6. Bradley, P. B., Deniker, P., Radouco-Thomas, C., Editors: *Neuro-Psychopharmacology. Proc. of 1st Internat. Congr. of Neuropharmacology, Rome, 1958.* Amsterdam, Elsevier, 1959.

7. Magoun, H. W., (p. 26), Beach, F. A., (p. 151), Gerard, R. W., (p. 163), Pribram, K. H., (p. 173), Ganong, W. F., (p. 64): Present volume.

8. Ingram, W. R., Hannet, F. I., and Ranson, S. W.: The topography of the nuclei of the diencephalon of the cat. *J. Comp. Neurol.* 55:333, 1932.

9. Ingram, W. R.: Nuclear organization and chief connections of the primate hypothalamus. *Proc. A. Res. Nerv. & Ment. Dis.* 20:195, 1940.

10. Clark, W. E. L., Beattie, J., Reddock, G., and Dott, N. M.: *The Hypothalamus; Morphological, Functional, Clinical and Surgical Aspects.* Edinburgh, London, Oliver & Boyd, 1938.

11. Jasper, H. H., Proctor, L. D., Knighton, R. S., Noshay, W. C., and Costello, R. T., Editors: *Reticular Formation of the Brain. Henry Ford Hospital Internat. Symposium,* Boston, Little, Brown & Co., 1958.

12. Papez, J. W. A proposed mechanism of emotion. *Arch. Neurol. & Psychiat.* 38:725, 1937.

13. MacLean, P. D. The limbic system ("visceral brain") in relation to central gray and reticulum of the brain stem. *Psychosom. Med.* 17:355, 1955.

14. Adey, W. R.: Organization of the rhinencephalon. In *Reticular Formation of the Brain. Henry Ford Hospital Internat. Symposium.* H. H. Jasper et al., Eds., Boston, Little, Brown & Co., 1958, p. 621.

15. Putnam, T. J., Frantz, A. M., Ranson, S. W., Editors: *The Diseases of the Basal Ganglia. Proc. A. Res. Nerv. & Ment. Dis.,* Vol. XXI, Baltimore, Williams & Wilkins, 1942.

16. Nauta, W. J. H., and Whitlock, D. G.: An anatomical analysis of the non-specific thalamic projection system. In *Brain Mechanisms and Consciousness: A Symposium. Council for Internat. Organizations of Medical Sciences.* J. F. Delafresnaye, Ed., Oxford, Blackwell Scientific Publications, 1954, p. 81.

17. Olszewski, J.: The cytoarchitecture of the human reticular formation. In *Brain Mechanisms and Consciousness: A Symposium. Council for Internat. Organizations of Medical Sciences.* J. F. Delafresnaye, Ed., Oxford, Blackwell Scientific Publications, 1954, p. 54.

18. Scheibel, M. E., and Scheibel, A. B.: Structural substrates for integrative patterns in the brain stem reticular core. In *Reticular Formation of the Brain. Henry Ford Hospital Internat. Symposium.* H. H. Jasper et al., Eds., Boston, Little, Brown & Co., 1958, p. 31.

19. Olszewski, J. Loc. cit. (ref. 17) p. 72.

20. Nauta, W. J. H., and Kuypers, H. G. J. M.: Some ascending pathways in the brain stem reticular formation. In *Reticular*

Formation of the Brain. Henry Ford Hospital Internat. Symposium, H. H. Jasper et al., Eds., Boston, Little, Brown & Co., 1958, p. 3.

21. Nauta, W. J. H.: Hippocampal projections and related neural pathways to the mid-brain in the cat. *Brain 81:*319, 1958.

22. Nauta, W. J. H.: Loc. cit. (Ref. No. 21), p. 339.

23. Pribram, K. H., and Kruger, L.: Functions of the "olfactory brain." *Ann. New York Acad. Sc. 58:*109, 1954.

24. Gloor, P.: Electrophysiological studies on the connections of the amygdaloid nucleus in the cat. II. The electrophysiological properties of the amygdaloid projection system. *Electroencephalog. & Clin. Neurophysiol. 7:*243, 1955.

25. Brady, J. V.: The paleocortex and behavioral motivation. In *Biological and Biochemical Bases of Behavior. Symposium on Interdisciplinary Research, Univ. of Wisconsin, 1955.* H. F. Harlow, and C. N. Woolsey, Eds., Madison, Univ. of Wisconsin Press, 1958, p. 193.

26. Olds, J.: Adaptive functions of paleocortical and related structures. In *Biological and Biochemical Bases of Behavior. Symposium on Interdisciplinary Research, Univ. of Wisconsin, 1955.* H. F. Harlow, and C. N. Woolsey, Eds., Madison, Univ. of Wisconsin Press, 1958, p. 237.

27. Ranson, S. W.: Regulation of body temperature. *Proc. A Res. Nerv. & Ment. Dis. 20:*342, 1940.

28. Brobeck, J. R.: Neural regulation of food intake. *Ann. New York Acad. Sc. 63:*44, 1955.

29. Hess, W. R.: *Das Zwischenhirn: Syndrome, Lokalisationen, Funktionen.* Basel, Schwabe, 1949.

30. Hare, K., and Geohegan, W. A.: Influence of frequency of stimulus upon the response to hypothalamic stimulation. *J. Neurophysiol. 4:*266, 1941.

31. Gellhorn, E., Cortell, R., and Murphy, J. P.: Are mass discharges characteristic of central autonomic structures? *Am. J. Physiol. 146:*376, 1946.

32. Olds, J., and Milner, P.: Positive reinforcement produced by electrical stimulation of septal area and other regions of rat brain. *J. Comp. & Physiol. Psychol. 47:*419, 1954.

33. Olds, J.: Selective effects of drives and drugs on "reward" systems of the brain. In *Neurological Basis of Behaviour. Ciba Foundation Symposium, London, 1957.* G. E. W. Wolsten-

holme, and C. M. O'Connor, Eds., London, J. & A. Churchill, 1958, p. 124.

34. Olds, J.: Studies of neuropharmacologicals by electrical and chemical manipulation of the brain in animals with chronically implanted electrodes. In *Neuro-Psychopharmacology. Proc. of 1st Internat. Congr. of Neuro-pharmacology, Rome, 1958.* P. B. Bradley, P. Deniker, and C. Radouco-Thomas, Eds., Amsterdam, Elsevier, 1959, p. 20.

35. Kaada, B. R., Andersen, P., and Jansen, J., Jr.: Stimulation of the amygdaloid nuclear complex in unanesthetized cats. *Neurology* 4:48, 1954.

36. Andersson, B., Jewell, P. A., and Larsson, S.: An appraisal of the effects of diencephalic stimulation of conscious animals in terms of normal behaviour. In *Neurological Basis of Behaviour. Ciba Foundation Symposium, London, 1957.* G. E. W. Wolstenholme, and C. M. O'Connor, Eds., London, J. and A. Churchill, 1958, p. 76.

37. Klüver, H., and Bucy, P. C.: "Psychic blindness" and other symptoms following bilateral temporal lobectomy in Rhesus monkeys. *Am. J. Physiol. 119:*352, 1937.

38. Bard, P., and Mountcastle, V. B.: Some forebrain mechanisms involved in expression of rage with special reference to suppression of angry behavior. *Proc. A. Res. Nerv. & Ment. Dis.* 27:362, 1948.

39. Schreiner, L., and Kling, A.: Behavioral changes following rhinencephalic injury in cat. *J. Neurophysiol. 16:*643, 1953.

40. Fuller, J. L., Rosvold, H. E., and Pribram, K. H.: The effect on affective and cognitive behavior in the dog of lesions of the pyriform-amygdala-hippocampal complex. *J. Comp. & Physiol. Psychol. 50:*89, 1957.

41. MacLean, P. D.: Chemical and electrical stimulation of hippocampus in unrestrained animals. I. Methods and electroencephalographic findings. *A.M.A. Arch. Neurol. & Psychiat. 78:*113, 1957.

42. Richter, C. P.: Neurological basis of responses to stress. In *Neurological Basis of Behavior. Ciba Foundation Symposium, London, 1957.* G. E. W. Wolstenholme, and C. M. O'Connor, Eds., London, J. & A. Churchill, 1958, p. 204.

43. Mason, J. W.: The central nervous system regulation of ACTH secretion. In *Reticular Formation of the Brain. Henry Ford*

Hospital Internat. Symposium. H. H. Jasper et al., Eds., Boston, Little, Brown & Co., 1958, p. 645.

44. Salmoiraghi, G. C., and Burns, B. C.: Localization and patterns of discharge of respiratory neurones. *J. Neurophysiol.* (In Press.)

45. Miller, N. E.: Objective techniques for studying motivational effects of drugs on animals. In: *Psychotropic Drugs.* S. Garattini and V. Ghetti, Eds., Amsterdam, Elsevier, 1957, p. 83.

46. Brady, J. V.: Differential drug effects upon aversive and appetitive components of a behavioral repertoire. In *Neuro-Psychopharmacology. Proc. of 1st Internat. Congr. of Neuro-pharmacology, Rome, 1958.* Amsterdam, Elsevier, 1959.

47. Masserman, J. H., and Yum, K. S.: An analysis of the influence of alcohol on experimental neuroses in cats. *Psychosom. Med.* 8:36, 1946.

48. Bradley, P. B., and Elkes, J.: A technique for recording the electrical activity of the brain in the conscious animal. *Electroencephalog. & Clin. Neurophysiol.* 5:451, 1953.

49. Bradley, P. B., and Elkes, J.: The effect of amphetamine and D-lysergic acid diethylamide (LSD 25) on the electrical activity of the brain of the conscious cat. *J. Physiol. 120:* 13P, 1953.

50. Bradley, P. B., and Elkes, J.: The effect of atropine, hyoscyamine, physostigmine and neostigmine on the electrical activity of the brain of the conscious cat. *J. Physiol. 120:*14P, 1953.

51. Bradley, P. B., and Elkes, J.: The effects of some drugs on the electrical activity of the brain. *Brain 80:*77, 1957.

52. Elkes, J.: Effects of psychosomimetic drugs in animals and man. In *Third Conference on Neuropharmacology, Princeton, 1956.* H. A. Abramson, Ed., New York, Josiah Macy, Jr. Foundation, 1957, p. 205.

53. Elkes, J.: Drug effects in relation to receptor specificity within the brain: some evidence and provisional formulation. In *Neurological Basis of Behavior. Ciba Foundation Symposium, London, 1957.* G. E. W. Wolstenholme, and C. M. O'Connor, Eds., London, J. & A. Churchill, 1958, p. 303.

54. Wikler, A.: Pharmacologic dissociation of behavior and EEG "sleep patterns" in dogs: morphine, N-allylnormorphine, and atropine. *Proc. Soc. Exper. Biol. & Med.* 79:261, 1952.

55. Bremer, F.: Cerveau «isolé» et physiologie du sommeil. *Compt. rend. Soc. de biol. 118:*1235, 1935.

56. Moruzzi, G., and Magoun, H. W.: Brain stem reticular formation and activation of the EEG. *Electroencephalog. & Clin. Neurophysiol. 1:*455, 1949.

57. Magoun, H. W.: The ascending reticular activating system. *Proc. A. Res. Nerv. & Ment. Dis. 30:*480, 1952.

58. Hiebel, G., Bonvallet, M., Huve, P., and Dell, P.: Analyse neurophysiologique de l'action centrale de la d-amphétamine (maxiton). *Semaine hôp. Paris. 30:*1880, 1954.

59. Vogt, M.: The concentration of sympathin in different parts of the central nervous system under normal conditions and after the administration of drugs. *J. Physiol. 123:*451, 1954.

60. Dell, P. C.: Humoral effects on the brain stem reticular formations. In *Reticular Formation of the Brain. Henry Ford Hospital Internat. Symposium.* H. H. Jasper et al., Eds., Boston, Little, Brown & Co., 1958, p. 365.

61. Rothballer, A. B.: Studies on the adrenaline-sensitive component of the reticular activating system. *Electroencephalog. & Clin. Neurophysiol. 8:*603, 1956.

62. Bradley, P. B., and Hance, A. J.: The effect of chlorpromazine and methopromazine on the electrical activity of the brain in the cat. *Electroencephalog. & Clin. Neurophysiol. 9:*191, 1957.

63. Bradley, P. B.: The central action of certain drugs in relation to the reticular formation of the brain. In *Reticular Formation of the Brain. Henry Ford Hospital Internat. Symposium.* H. H. Jasper et al., Eds., Boston, Little, Brown & Co., 1958, p. 123.

64. Bradley, P. B., and Key, B. J.: A comparative study of the effects of drugs on the arousal system of the brain. *Br. J. Pharmacol. 14:*340, 1959.

65. Killam, K. F., and Killam, E. K.: Drug action on pathways involving the reticular formation. In *Reticular Formation of the Brain. Henry Ford Hospital Internat. Symposium.* H. H. Jasper et al., Eds., Boston, Little, Brown & Co., 1958, p. 111.

66. Pfeiffer, C. C., Jenney, E. H., Gallagher, W., Smith, R. P., Bevan, W., Jr., Killam, K. F., Killam, E. K. and Blackmore, W.: Stimulant effect of 2-dimethylaminoethanol; possible precursor of brain acetylcholine. *Science 126:*610, 1957.

67. Killam, E. K., Gangloff, H., Konigsmark, B., and Killam, K. F.: The action of pharmacologic agents on evoked cortical activity. In *Biological Psychiatry. Proc. of Scientific Sessions of Soc. of Biol. Psychiat., San Francisco, 1958.* J. H. Masserman, Ed., New York, Grune & Stratton, 1959, p. 53.

68. Himwich, H. E., Van Meter, W. G., and Owens, H.: Drugs used in the treatment of the depressions. In *Biological Psychiatry. Proc. of Scientific Sessions of Soc. of Biol. Psychiat., San Francisco, 1958.* J. H. Masserman, Ed., New York, Grune & Stratton, 1959, p. 27.

69. Elkes, J.: Discussion of Himwich, H., et al., (Ref. No. 68), p. 50.

70. Jacobsen, E., and Skaarup, Y.: Experimental induction of conflict-behaviour in cats: the effect of some anticholinergic compounds. *Acta pharmacol. et toxicol.* (KbH) *11:*125, 1955.

71. Sigg, E. B.: Pharmacological studies with tofranil. *Canad. Psychiat. A. J.* 4:75, 1959.

72. Amassian, V. E., and Waller, H. J.: Spatiotemporal patterns of activity in individual reticular neurons. In *Reticular Formation of the Brain. Henry Ford Hospital Internat. Symposium.* H. H. Jasper et al., Eds., Boston, Little, Brown & Co., 1958, p. 69.

73. Bradley, P. B.: Microelectrode approach to the neuropharmacology of the reticular formation. In *Psychotropic Drugs.* S. Garattini and V. Ghetti, Eds., Amsterdam, Elsevier, 1957, p. 207.

74. Bradley, P. B., and Mollica, A.: The effect of adrenaline and acetylcholine on single unit activity in the reticular formation of the decerebrate cat. *Arch. ital. biol.* 94:168, 1958.

75. Whitfield, I. C., Schwartz, A., and Fotheringham, J. B.: Unpublished findings.

76. Feldberg, W., and Vogt, M.: Acetylcholine synthesis in different regions of central nervous system. *J. Physiol.* 107:372, 1948.

77. Feldberg, W.: Present views on mode of action of acetylcholine in central nervous system. *Physiol. Rev.* 25:596, 1945.

78. Weil-Malherbe, H., and Bone, A. D.: Intracellular distribution of catecholamines in the brain. *Nature* (London) *180:*1050, 1957.

79. Carlsson, A.: The occurrence, distribution and physiological role of catecholamines in the nervous system. *Pharmacol. Rev. 11:* 490, 1959.

80. Blaschko, H., Hagen, J. M., and Hagen, P.: Mitochondrial enzymes and chromaffin-granules. *J. Physiol.* 139:316, 1957.

81. Falck, B., Hillarp, N. A., and Högberg, B.: Content and intracellular distribution of adenosine triphosphate in cow adrenal medulla. *Acta physiol. scandinav.* 36:360, 1956.

82. Holtz, P., and Westerman, E.: Über die Dopadecarboxylase und Histidindecarboxylase des Nervengewebes. *Arch. exper. Path. u. Pharmakol.* 227:538, 1956.

83. Udenfriend, S., and Wyngaarden, J. B.: Precursors of adrenal epinephrine and norepinephrine in vivo. *Biochim. et biophys. acta* 20:48, 1956.

84. Rosenfeld, G., Leeper, L. C., and Udenfriend, S.: Biosynthesis of norepinephrine and epinephrine by the isolated perfused calf adrenal. *Fed. Proc.* 16:331, 1957.

85. Kirshner, N., and Goodall, McC.: Formation of adrenaline from noradrenaline. *Fed. Proc.* 16:73, 1957.

86. Weil-Malherbe, H., Axelrod, J., and Tomchick, R.: Blood-brain barrier for adrenaline. *Science* 129:1226, 1959.

87. Weil-Malherbe, H., and Bone, A. D.: The effect of reserpine on the intracellular distribution of catecholamines in the brain stem of the rabbit. *J. Neurochem.* 4:251, 1959.

88. Kety, S. S.: The possible relationships between the catecholamines and emotional states. (p. 77) Present volume.

89. Armstrong. M. D.: McMillan, A., and Shaw, K. N. F.: 3-Methoxy-4-hydroxy-D-mandelic acid, a urinary metabolite of norepinephrine. *Biochim. et biophys. acta* 25:422, 1957.

90. Symposium on Catecholamines. *Pharmacol. Rev. 11 (2-Part 2):* 232, 1959.

91. Twarog, B. M., and Page, I. H.: Serotonin content of some mammalian tissues and urine and a method for its determination. *Am. J. Physiol.* 175:157, 1953.

92. Amin, A. H., Crawford, T. B. B., and Gaddum, J. H.: The distribution of substance P and 5-hydroxy-tryptamine in the central nervous system of the dog. *J. Physiol.* 126:596, 1954.

93. Paasonen, M. K., MacLean, P. D., and Giarman, N. J.: 5-Hydroxytryptamine (serotonin, enteramine) content of structures of the limbic system. *J. Neurochem.* 1:326, 1957.

94. Gaddum, J. H., and Giarman, N. J.: Preliminary studies on the biosynthesis of 5-hydroxytryptamine. *Brit. J. Pharmacol.* 11:88, 1956.

95. Udenfriend, S., Bogdanski, D. F., and Weissbach, H.: Biochemistry and metabolism of serotonin as it relates to the nervous system. In *Metabolism of the Nervous System. Internat. Neurochemical Symposium, Aarhus, Denmark, 1957.* D. Richter, Ed., New York, Pergamon Press, 1957, p. 566.

96. Shore, P. A., Mead, J. A., Kuntzman, R. G., Spector, S., and Brodie, B. B.: On the physiologic significance of monoamine oxidase in brain. *Science 126:*1063, 1957.

97. Corne, S. J., and Graham, J. D. :The effect of inhibition of amine oxidase in vivo on administered adrenaline, noradrenaline, tyramine and serotonin. *J. Physiol. 135:*339, 1957.

98. Sjoerdsma, A., Gillespie, L., Jr., and Udenfriend, S.: A simple method for the measurement of monoamine-oxidase inhibition in man. Lancet 2:159, 1958.

99. Udenfriend, S., and Weissbach, H.: Turnover of 5-hydroxytryptamine (serotonin) in tissues. *Proc. Soc. Exper. Biol. & Med. 97:*748, 1958.

100. Purpura, D. P., Girado, M., Smith, T. G., Callan, D. A., and Grundfest, H.: Structure-activity determinants of pharmacological effects of amino acids and related compounds on central synapses. *J. Neurochem. 3:*238, 1959.

101. Roberts, E., Harman, P. J., and Frankel, S.: γ-Aminobutyric acid content and glutamic decarboxylase activity in developing mouse brain. *Proc. Soc. Exper. Biol. & Med. 78:*799, 1951.

102. Roberts, E.: Formation and utilization of γ-aminobutyric acid in brain. *Progress in Neurobiology 1:*11, 1956.

103. Roberts, E.: The biochemistry of gamma aminobutyric acid in the central nervous system. *Proc. of the Western Pharmacology Soc.* (Seattle, McCaffrey Dogwood Press) *1:*29, 1958.

104. Salvador, R. A., and Albers, R. W.: The distribution of glutamic γ-aminobutyric transaminase in the nervous system of the rhesus monkey. *J. Biol. Chem. 234:*922, 1959.

105. Albers, R. W., and Brady, R. O.: The distribution of glutamic decarboxylase in the nervous system of the rhesus monkey. *J. Biol. Chem. 234:*926, 1959.

106. Baxter, C. F., and Roberts: E. (In press.)

107. Killam, K. F.: Convulsant hydrazides. II. Comparison of electrical changes and enzyme inhibition induced by administration of thiosemicarbazide. *J. Pharmacol. & Exper. Therap. 119:*263, 1957.

108. Dasgupta, S. R., Killam, E. K., and Killam, K. F.: Drug action on rhinencephalic seizure activity in the cat. *J. Pharmacol. & Exper. Therap. 122:*16A, 1958.

109. Eidelberg, E., Baxter, C. F., Roberts, E., Saldias, C. A., and French, J. D.: In *Inhibition in the Nervous System and γ-*

Aminobutyric Acid. Proc. of Symposium Sponsored by Air Force Office of Scientific Research, Duarte, Calif., 1959. E. Roberts, Ed., New York, Pergamon Press. (In press.)

110. Florey, E., and McLennan, H.: Effects of an inhibitory factor (factor I) from brain on central synaptic transmission. *J. Physiol. 130:*446, 1955.

111. Roberts, E., Editor. *Inhibition in the Nervous System and γ-Aminobutyric Acid. Proc. of Symposium Sponsored by Air Force Office of Scientific Research, Durarte, Calif., 1959.* New York, Pergamon Press. (In press.)

112. Waelsch, H. W.: Metabolism of proteins and amino acids. In *Metabolism of the Nervous System. Internat. Neurochemical Symposium, Aarhus, Denmark, 1956.* D. Richter, Ed., New York, Pergamon Press, 1957, p. 431.

113. Strecker, H. J.: Glutamic acid and glutamine. In *Metabolism of the Nervous System. Internat. Neurochemical Symposium, Aarhus, Denmark, 1957.* D. Richter, Ed., New York, Pergamon Press, 1957, p. 459.

114. Waelsch, H. W.: New aspects of amine metabolism. In *The Chemical Pathology of the Nervous System.* J. Folch-Pi, Ed., London, Pergamon Press. (In press.)

115. Vogt, M.: Catecholamines in brain. *Pharmacol. Rev. 11:*483, 1959.

116. Brodie, B. B., Pletscher, A., and Shore, P. A.: Evidence that serotonin has a role in brain function. *Science 122:*968, 1955.

117. Brodie, B. B., Pletscher, A., and Shore, P. A.: Possible role of serotonin in brain function and in reserpine action. *J. Pharmacol. & Exper. Therap. 116:*9, 1956.

118. Pletscher, A., Shore, P. A., and Brodie, B. B.: Serotonin as a mediator of reserpine action in brain. *J. Pharmacol. & Exper. Therap. 116:*84, 1956.

119. Pletscher, A., Shore, P. A., and Brodie, B. B.: Release of brain serotonin by reserpine. *J. Pharmacol. & Exper. Therap. 116:*46, 1956.

120. Holzbauer, M., and Vogt, M.: Depression by reserpine of the noradrenaline concentration in the hypothalamus of the cat. *J. Neurochem. 1:*8, 1956.

121. Weil-Malherbe, H.: Personal communication.

122. Giarman, N. J., and Schanberg, S.: The intracellular distribution of 5-hydroxytryptamine (HT; serotonin) in the rat's brain. *Biochem. Pharmacol. 1:*301, 1959.

123. Bülbring, E., and Burn, J. H.: Observations bearing on synaptic transmission by acetylcholine in the spinal cord. *J. Physiol. 100:*337, 1941.

124. Bülbring, E.: The action of adrenaline on transmission in the superior cervical ganglion. *J. Physiol. 103:*55, 1944.

125. Bülbring, E., and Burn, J. H.: An action of adrenaline on transmission in the sympathetic ganglia, which may play a part in shock. *J. Physiol. 101:*289, 1942.

126. Schweitzer, A., and Wright, S.: The action of adrenaline on the knee jerk. *J. Physiol. 88:*476, 1937.

127. Elkes, J.: On possible uses of pharmacological method in psychiatric research. In: *Prospects in Psychiatric Research. Proc. Oxford Conference of Mental Health Research Fund, March, 1952.* J. M. Tanner, Ed., Oxford, Blackwell Scientific Publications, 1953, p. 126.

128. Bülbring, E., Burn, J. H., and Skoglund, C. R.: The action of acetylcholine and adrenaline on flexor and extensor movements evoked by stimulation of the descending motor tracts. *J. Physiol. 107:*289, 1948.

129. Burn, J. H.: The relation of adrenaline to acetylcholine in the nervous system. *Physiol. Rev. 25:*377, **1945.**

130. Ramey, E. R., and Goldstein, M. S.: Adrenal cortex and the sympathetic nervous system. *Physiol. Rev. 37:*155, 1957.

131. De Maio, D.: Influence of adrenalectomy and hypophysectomy on cerebral serotonin. *Science 129:*1678, 1959.

132. Garattini, S., and Valzelli, L.: Researches on the mechanism of reserpine sedative action. *Science 128:*1278, 1958.

133. Brodie, B. B., Finger, K. F., Orlans, F. B., Quinn, G. P., and Sulser, F.: Evidence that tranquilizing action of reserpine is associated with change in brain serotonin and not in brain norepinephrine. 1960. (In press.)

134. Harris, G. W., Michael, R. P., and Scott, P. P.: Neurological site of action of stilboestrol in eliciting sexual behavior. In: *Neurological Basis of Behavior, Ciba Foundation Symposium, London, 1957.* G. E. W. Wolstenholme, and C. M. O'Connor, Eds., London, J. & A. Churchill, 1958, p. 236.

135. Sawyer, C. H.: Activation and blockade of the release of pituitary gonadotropin as influenced by the reticular formation. *In Reticular Formation of the Brain. Henry Ford Hospital Inter-*

nat. Symposium. H. H. Jasper, et al., Eds., Boston, Little, Brown & Co., 1958, p. 223.

136. Persky, H., Hamburg, D. A., Basowitz, H., Grinker, R. R., Sabshin, M., Korchin, S. J., Herz, M., Board, F. A., and Heath, H. A.: Relation of emotional responses and changes in plasma hydrocortisone level after stressful interview. *A.M.A. Arch. Neurol. & Psychiat.* 79:434, 1958.

137. Board, F., Wadeson, R., and Persky, H.: Depressive affect and endocrine functions. *A. M. A. Arch. Neurol. & Psychiat.* 78: 612, 1957.

138. Mason, J. W., and Hamburg, D. A.: Quoted by S. S. Kety, present volume.

139. Waelsch, H., Editor: *Ultrastructure and Cellular Chemistry of Neural Tissue. Progress in Neurobiology,* Vol. II, New York, Hoeber-Harper, 1957.

140. Sokoloff, L.: Local blood flow in neural tissue. In *New Research Techniques in Neuroanatomy. A Symposium Sponsored by the Nat. Multiple Sclerosis Soc.* W. F. Windle, Ed., Charles C. Thomas, 1957, p. 51.

141. Waelsch, H. W.: Personal communication.

142. Elkes, J., Elkes, C., and Bradley, P. B.: The effect of some drugs on the electrical activity of the brain, and on behavior. *J. Ment. Sc. 100:*125, 1954.

143. Lerner, A. B., Case, J. D., Takahashi, Y., Lee, T. H., and Mori, W.: Isolation of melanotonin, the pineal gland factor that lightens melanocytes. *J. Am. Chem. Soc. 80:*2587, 1958.

144. Nurnberger, J. I., and Gordon, M. W.: The cell density of neural tissues: Direct counting method and possible applications as a biologic referent. *Progress in Neurobiology 2:*100, 1957.

145. Pope, A., Hess, H. H., and Allen, J. N.: Quantitative histochemistry of proteolytic and oxidative enzymes in human cerebral cortex and brain tumors. *Progress in Neurobiology 2:*182, 1957.

146. Robins, E., Smith, D. E., and Jen, M. K.: The quantitative distribution of eight enzymes of glucose metabolism and two citric acid cycle enzymes in the cerebellar cortex and its subjacent white matter. *Progress in Neurobiology 2:*205, 1957.

147. Koelle, G. B.: The localization of acetylcholinesterase in neurons. *Progress in Neurobiology 2:*164, 1957.

148. Berger, M.: Effect of chlorpromazine on oxidative phosphoryla-
tion of liver and brain mitochondria. *Progress in Neurobiology*
2:158, 1957.

149. Olds, J., and Olds, M. E.: Positive reinforcement produced by
stimulating hypothalamus with iproniazid and other compounds. *Science 127:1175,* 1958.

150. John, E. R., and Killam, K. F.: Electrophysiological correlates
of avoidance conditioning in the cat. *J. Pharmacol. & Exper.
Therap. 125:252,* 1959.

DISCUSSION

Dr. R. M. Featherstone: Dr. Elkes represents a somewhat rare
phenomenon: one who is as firmly established in the field of
psychiatry as in pharmacology. In the interdisciplinary training
programs planned for this area and already under way at some
other institutions, we hope to develop persons who can hold
between the ears of one head considerable knowledge and critical
judgment in these various fields. As we pharmacologists discuss
topics with our colleagues from other lines of endeavor, we find
that the psychiatrist, for example, may be naïve about recent developments in pharmacology, just as the pharmacologist may be
naïve with respect to psychiatry.

It is somewhat unusual for a "molecular level pharmacologist"
to find himself on the platform during a meeting related to the
emotions. We are far from being ready to say much about the
relationship of molecular phenomena to emotions, despite the
brilliant work that has led to the determination of levels of various
compounds in blood, urine, and sites within other tissues, particularly the brain. Such discoveries have been helpful, but we must
look ahead to see the kinds of problem that remain.

It is questionable whether the level of any substance in any body
site has specific significance. That level is the result of many factors
including, as Dr. Elkes has shown, the enzymes that synthesize
the material, the enzymes that destroy it, and other phenomena
such as absorption, distribution, and metabolism at various sites.
Even within a single cell there are several types of membrane
which must be traversed by some of these compounds or by their

precursors. It is therefore appropriate that attention is being directed toward these problems.

Where adequate chemical means are available for the detection of specific substances, we are fairly certain that we are dealing with those substances. This is true in the cases of epinephrine, norepinephrine, and serotonin for example; but it is not always the case with acetylcholine, a compound with which I have spent more time than with some others. Many of us have been frustrated by finding that when we have worked our way to some substance that we believe to be acetylcholine, and then apply a test which should identify it clearly as such, the material eludes the test, proving itself not to be acetylcholine. If we are going to think about the actions of the compounds discussed today, we must clarify such points as these.

The effects of many of these drugs are not apparent until some time after they have been given. This suggests the possibility that we are bringing about certain changes in enzyme levels in highly local sites within brain cells. I am a little frightened by the complexity of the brain cells, as it has been presented during this meeting. This means that the chemist must greatly refine techniques; we must work much more closely with the anatomist and pathologist to make histochemistry a more respectable science than it has been in the past.

It is a matter for regret that so many excellent pharmacology investigators are not addressing such fundamental problems as those that have been apparent in the program presented today. I refer to many of those who are working in industry. Their efforts are directed somewhat to the production or the recognition of compounds which do the same thing that many other compounds do. Rather than having seventeen more pentothiazines, I believe it would be far more important if in some way we could bring about the reorientation of effort of these people toward the fundamental aspects of the problem.

VI

SEX DIFFERENCES IN THE PHYSIOLOGICAL BASES OF MATING BEHAVIOR IN MAMMALS

FRANK A. BEACH, Ph.D.

INTRODUCTION

THE evidence which I have to present deals exclusively with lower mammals, but I suspect that it has important implications for the interpretation of some aspects of human sexual life.

The story I have to tell began with an accidental discovery made in the course of some experiments on laboratory rats.

BRAIN MECHANISMS IN RATS

One experiment was designed to investigate the effects of neocortical lesions upon sexual behavior in male rats.[1] Normal males were observed in standardized mating tests before and after removal of varying amounts and areas of the cerebral cortex.

It was found that lesions involving less than 10 or 15% of the total neopallium had no detectable effect upon mating behavior, regardless of their locus. In contrast, destruction of 60% or more of the cerebral cortex totally eliminated sexual activity. Lesions invading from 20 to 50% of the cortex tended to reduce the probability that mating would occur postoperatively, and the extent of this reduction was proportional to the amount of cortical tissue removed.

It is important to add that cortically operated males, when they did mate with the receptive female, did so in normal fashion. In other words they were not physically incapacitated, nor did they

151

appear to suffer extensive sensory loss. The primary effect of extensive invasion of the neocortex seemed to be a reduction in the male's susceptibility to sexual arousal. This conclusion was substantiated by the additional finding that some cortically operated males which had ceased to copulate following operation could be induced to resume doing so if they were injected with very large amounts of androgenic hormone, which is known to intensify sexual excitability.

In a second experiment female rats were rendered sexually receptive by administration of the appropriate ovarian hormones. They were then placed with sexually active males and their mating behavior was scored on an objective scale.[2] Following the preoperative tests the females were surgically deprived of varying amounts and regions of the cerebral cortex. The results are easily summarized. Totally decorticated females continued to show intensely receptive sexual behavior when they were placed with normal males. The responses of females lacking all neocortex did not consist merely of the reflexive, postural adjustments necessary for successful coition in this species. Instead they included a high level of activity which stimulated the male to carry out his part of the mating pattern. The behavior of the decorticated females was not entirely normal, for there were obvious signs of disorientation, and some disintegration of the patterning of successive responses. Nevertheless, the behavior was sufficiently effective to arouse the male and permit him to mate and fertilize the female.

The results of these two experiments suggest that within the same species one sex must possess a certain amount of cerebral cortical tissue in order to become aroused and carry out the mating pattern, whereas the opposite sex is capable of effective sexual activity in total absence of the neopallium. By a stroke of good luck it became possible to verify these findings in a rather dramatic way.

It is known that female rats frequently mount other females in masculine fashion.[3] This occurs most commonly when the second, or stimulus, female is in a state of high sexual receptivity. The mounting behavior is not in any sense abnormal, but can be regarded as part of the female rat's normal sexual repertoire. The behavior is not as complete as that of the copulating male, but it often involves most of the elements of the normal masculine pattern.

Taking advantage of this fact, I measured the feminine sexual pattern and the masculine mounting activity in one and the same group of female rats.[4] Thereafter I removed the cerebral cortex and after the rats had recuperated they were retested for both feminine and masculine activity. Without exception it was found that the masculine pattern had been eliminated by cortical destruction, but the feminine sexual responses survived. This would seem to clinch the point that in this species masculine behavior, whether it is shown by genetic males or by females, depends upon cortical mechanisms, whereas the feminine pattern does not.

SEX DIFFERENCES IN OTHER PHYSIOLOGICAL MECHANISMS

At this stage of the investigation it was natural to ask why this particular difference between males and females should exist; and in an attempt to answer the question it was necessary to study the sensory cues involved in sexual arousal and mating behavior in males and females.

The experimental procedure involved depriving an animal of one or more types of sensory receptors, and then examining the responses to a sexually active partner. It was found that male rats are capable of mating with a receptive female after they have been deprived of the eyes, or the olfactory bulbs, or the receptors for cutaneous sensation in the snout, lips and other anterior head regions. When two of these three sensory avenues were destroyed in the same individual, the probability that mating would occur was significantly reduced, but at least in some males sexual activity persisted. Elimination of all three receptor systems totally eliminated mating behavior.[5]

Other experimental methods were used in attempting to answer the question, but in general the results seem fairly clear-cut. It was concluded that as far as the male rat is concerned no single type of sensory cue is indispensible as long as others remain. If a sufficient number of sensory inputs are destroyed in the same individual, sexual arousal will not occur.

More recent experiments have revealed that once sexual arousal has proceeded to the point that copulatory responses occur, a new source of stimulation becomes important. Using nonsurgical procedures, it was determined that if a male rat is to continue showing mating responses to a receptive female it is essential that he be able to achieve intromission. The opportunity to pursue and mount an estrous female does not provide sufficient stimulation to insure continued sexual activity. On the other hand, achievement of ejaculation and the accompanying orgasm are not essential, for when ejaculation is prevented copulatory responses continue indefinitely. Apparently, although it is not essential to the initial arousal of the male rat, genital stimulation derived from intromission is indispensible for continuation of the copulatory pattern.[6]

Equally systematic investigations on females have not been conducted, but evidence on several mammalian species summarized elsewhere[7] suggests that in this sex distance receptors are relatively less important for sexual arousal. The stimuli essential for mating in the female appear to be primarily derived from direct body contact. Thus the female rat's response depends on touch and deep pressure in the dorsal-lateral region just anterior to the pelvis. This is an area which is strongly stimulated by the male when he mounts the female and grips her with his forelegs.

Unlike the male of her species, the female rat does not need genital stimulation in order to remain receptive. Surgical removal of the vagina and the uterus, and closure of the external genital opening does not eliminate the female's willingness to allow the male to mount, nor does it have an effect upon her tendency to seek him out and actively court him if he is slow to approach her. Quite by chance we discovered one female rat with congenital absence of ovarian tissue and an imperforate vagina. When this individual was injected with estrogen and progesterone she became normally receptive and actively courted and received the male.[8]

The evidence summarized thus far suggests that the male rat depends upon cerebral cortical activity for his sexual arousal, and, in addition, his achievement of sexual excitation depends upon a multisensory pattern of stimulation provided by the female. The female, in contrast, may show sexually receptive behavior in the

absence of all exteroceptors, and when deprived of all genital
sensation.

One final difference in the physiological basis for sexual activity
in males and females of the species deserves mention. I refer to the
relative importance of gonadal hormones in males and females.
Normal sexual activity does not occur in males in the absence of
gonadal secretions, but the prepuberal male, or the adult castrate,
is not totally asexual. In late infancy male rats occasionally display
rudimentary forms of the adult masculine copulatory pattern.
They sometimes pursue other young animals and mount them
from the rear with a normal sexual clasp, meanwhile executing a
few, weak, pelvic thrusts.[9] A male which is castrated in adulthood
does not promptly lose all erotic responsiveness and potency. Although testicular hormone is metabolized rapidly, and presumably
has been completely dissipated within a matter of 24 hours after
operation, sexual behavior declines gradually, and in some instances
persists in incomplete form for several weeks.[10]

In contrast, the prepuberal female rat shows no feminine mating
activity whatsoever. She can be induced to do so if she is treated
with the proper combination of estrogen and progesterone, and
this means that the essential neuromuscular mechanisms are functional before they are normally called into play.[9]

Females which are deprived of their ovaries in adulthood become
unreceptive in a few hours and never again display any signs of
feminine responsiveness unless they are treated with estrogen, or
with estrogen and progesterone. It appears that although gonadal
hormones are important for complete sexual behavior in both males
and females, the male's dependence upon testicular hormone is at
least slightly less marked than is the dependence of the female upon
secretions of her ovaries.

SEX DIFFERENCES IN MATING BEHAVIOR

The neural and hormonal differences between males and females
described thus far are reflected in correlated differences of behavior. Male rats are susceptible to inhibition of sexual responsiveness by a variety of environmental stimuli which do not seem to
influence the female. Males which are confronted with receptive

females in an unfamiliar environment, or in a familiar one which has previously been associated with pain or fear, do not immediately engage in sexual activity. In many instances no mating behavior whatsoever occurs, and in others a prolonged period of investigation of the environment must precede attention to the sexual partner. Under comparable conditions, females which are in complete estrus respond promptly to the male's courtship behavior and mate without hesitation.[7]

Sexual arousal in male rats is often facilitated as a result of conditioning. If a male has mated successfully in a given cage or observation chamber he may, when returned to the same chamber, display sexual arousal and even attempt to copulate with biologically inadequate sexual partners such as other males, nonreceptive females, or even animals of a different species. A single association of sexual stimulation with initially neutral stimuli provided by the testing environment may result in conditioning which lasts for several weeks.[5] As a result the environmental stimuli come to evoke sexual arousal and facilitate mating. Comparable conditioning has not been observed in females of this species. No matter how many times they may have mated in a given environmental situation, females show no signs of becoming aroused on subsequent tests in that situation unless they are in the appropriate physiological condition for mating.

Finally, there is ample evidence to indicate that male rats will learn an instrumental response, or will master a maze, when the re-enforcement is opportunity to copulate with a receptive female.[11] Systematic attempts to duplicate these results with females have not been made, but preliminary experiments in my laboratory have yielded uniformly negative results.

I am inclined to adopt the working hypothesis that these behavioral differences between the sexes are functionally related to the relative importance of the cortical mechanisms in the male's sexual activity, and the lack of any essential cortical involvement as far as the female's mating behavior is concerned.

EXPERIMENTS UPON OTHER ANIMALS

It is, of course, important to discover if the sex differences which I have described are restricted to a single species, or whether they are characteristic of other mammals. The limited evidence that is available indicates that comparable differences exist in carnivores.

As long ago as 1892 the German physiologist Goltz reported that male dogs deprived of the forebrain showed no interest in the bitch in heat.[12] The same investigator observed, in contrast, that females of this species which have been subjected to complete section of the cord continue to display sexual receptivity when they are confronted with a normal male.[13]

Bard[14] found that complete transection of the brain at any point anterior to the midthalamic region does not eliminate mating behavior in female cats. An extensive study conducted in my own laboratory showed that certain types of cortical lesion produce severe disruptions of copulatory behavior in males of this species. Removal of the frontal cortex incapacitates the male cat as far as coitus is concerned, but this operation does not, so far as one can tell from direct observation, reduce the capacity for sexual arousal.[15] Destruction of the occipital regions of the cerebrum produces cortical blindness, and this is reflected in the male's inability to locate a distant female. However, this type of operation does not interfere with mating once physical contact has been established.[16] Total decortication results in complete and permanent loss of any mating tendency in the male cat.[17]

With respect to the importance of the gonadal hormones for sexual performance, the differences which exist between male and female rodents appear to be present also in carnivores. Female cats or dogs cannot be induced to display any signs of sexual receptivity unless they are physiologically in estrus. There are no signs of the adult feminine pattern in prepuberal females of these two species. and ovariectomized adults are totally unreceptive.[7]

The studies of Rosenblatt and Aronson have revealed that male cats may continue to mate for many weeks after removal of the testes.[18] Comparable results have been obtained in my laboratory using male dogs as experimental subjects. In both species one important factor is the amount of sexual experience that the male has acquired prior to gonadectomy. Sexually naïve males rarely exhibit complete mating behavior when they are tested with females after castration; but male cats and dogs that have mated in a long series of preoperative tests respond normally to the female for months and even years after loss of the testes. In carnivores, as in rodents, it seems that the female's sexual receptivity is tied closely to the secretion of ovarian hormones; whereas the male exhibits a surprising degree of independence from testicular hormones provided his preoperative experiential background includes a good deal of sexual activity.

I pointed out that male rats differ from females in that sexual arousal and mating performance are strongly affected by factors other than the immediate presence of a biologically adequate partner. The same is true in the case of carnivores. We have just noted that previous sexual experience is one important factor determining the effects of castration in the male, but not in the case of the female. In both cats and dogs the sexual responsiveness of the male may be totally inhibited by a strange environment or by a familiar one previously associated with fear, pain, or anxiety.[19]

It is exceedingly difficult to induce a male cat to show any interest in the receptive female when they are simply brought together in the laboratory. If copulation is to occur, it is very important that the male be thoroughly acclimatized to the laboratory and to the testing area. Some observers have concluded that the male must have time and opportunity to establish territorial rights over the region in which he is to be tested.[20] Others have reported the necessity of gradually conditioning the male to the receptive female before a consistent mating performance can be expected.[21]

Fewer than 50% of the adult male dogs tested for mating behavior in my laboratory have shown effective coital responses the first time they were confined with a bitch in estrus. In a number of instances it was necessary to hand-breed a male, and assist him in effecting sexual union once or perhaps several times before he would spontaneously copulate with a female.

Like the male rodent, the male dog can be sexually conditioned to a given environmental setting with the result that upon subsequent occasions his erotic arousal occurs much more rapidly, and he may show an indiscriminate tendency to mate with almost any other animal within an appropriate size range.

These behavioral differences between male and female carnivores seem again to be related to differences in the neurological mechanisms involved in the sexual response.

One incidental item of information which harmonizes with more systematic findings is that many male dogs appear to develop preferences for mating with particular females and aversions toward others, even though the latter may be in full estrus and quite willing to mate. Comparable preferences have not been reported for females of this species.

ARE THERE ANY COMPARABLE DIFFERENCES BETWEEN THE SEXES AT THE HUMAN LEVEL?

The question naturally presents itself as to whether or not the sex differences which exist in lower mammals have any counterparts in our own species. No direct answers are available and the search for such is fraught with many difficulties. In the first place science is regrettably ignorant with respect to the physiological mechanisms involved in human sexual responses, particularly in the arousal of erotic excitement. Furthermore, it is entirely possible that fundamental physiological differences might exist between the sexes but be completely obscured by the social and cultural channeling of sexual impulses and activities.

Perhaps the most comprehensive evidence bearing upon sex differences in human beings has been presented by Kinsey and his collaborators.[22] Kinsey's conclusions with respect to this problem are summarized in his statement that the human male has a much greater capacity to respond to "psychosexual" stimuli than does the female. This interpretation is based upon a variety of findings.

American men, in contradistinction to American women, are reported to be highly susceptible to sexual arousal by what might be termed representative or surrogate stimuli. Thus many more men than women are sexually excited by erotic pictures, jokes, and literature. Women tend to be aroused primarily by the direct stimulation provided by a sexual partner. Masturbation is much more common in males than in females, and when autoerotic behavior does occur it is often accompanied by sexual phantasy in males, but much less frequently in females. Erotic dreams are much more common in men than women. More men than women are sexually aroused by merely observing members of the opposite sex, clothed or nude.

With respect to the effects of previous experience upon sexual behavior, Kinsey and his collaborators have this to say:

> "In general, males are more often conditioned by their sexual experience, and by a greater variety of associated factors, than females. While there is great individual variation in this respect among both females and males, there is considerable evidence that the sexual responses and behavior of the average male are, on the whole, more often determined by the male's previous experience, by his association with objects that were connected with his previous sexual experience, by his vicarious sharing of another individual's sexual experience, and by his sympathetic reactions to the sexual responses of other individuals. The average female is less often affected by such psychologic factors. It is highly significant to find that there are evidences of such differences between the females and males of infra-human mammalian species, as well as between human females and males."[22,pp.649-650]

Ever since John B. Watson espoused the cult of American behaviorism, psychologists have championed the view that all or nearly all of the psychologic or behavioral differences between individuals, between the sexes, and between different racial groups are entirely determined by experience. The cross-cultural studies made by some anthropologists have revealed differences that have been similarly interpreted.

It seems to me the time has come for a re-examination of these problems with great attention being given to genetically-influenced, biologic factors which may contribute to some of these differences. In view of the evidence drawn from other species of mammals, I am presently inclined to believe that human males and females differ from one another with respect to the physiological mechanisms involved in sexual arousal and gratification. I suspect further that cultural and environmental forces, instead of producing all of the behavioral differences between the sexes, actually tend to obscure some of them, and to blur certain basic distinctions that are rooted in physiological differences which are part of our mammalian heritage.

REFERENCES

1. Beach, F. A.: Effects of cortical lesions upon the copulatory behavior of male rats. *J. Comp. Psychol., 29:*193, 1940.

2. Beach, F. A.: Effects of injury to the cerebral cortex upon sexually-receptive behavior in the female rat. *Psychosom. Med., 6:*40, 1944.

3. Beach, F. A.: Execution of the complete masculine copulatory pattern by sexually receptive female rats. *J. Genet. Psychol., 60:*137, 1942.

4. Beach, F. A.: Effects of injury to the cerebral cortex upon the display of masculine and feminine mating behavior by female rats. *J. Comp. Psychol., 36:*169, 1943.

5. Beach, F. A.: Anaylsis of the stimuli adequate to elicit mating behavior in the sexually inexperienced male rat. *J. Comp. Psychol., 33:*163, 1942.

6. Beach, F. A., and Whalen, R.: Effects of intromission without ejaculation upon sexual behavior in male rats. *J. Comp. & Physiol. Psychol., 52:*476, 1959.

7. Beach, F. A.: A review of physiological and psychological studies of sexual behavior in mammals. *Physiol. Rev.,* 27:240, 1947.

8. Beach, F. A.: Hormonal induction of mating responses in a rat with congenital absence of gonadal tissue. *Anat. Rec., 92:*289, 1945.

9. Beach, F. A.: Sexual behavior of prepuberal male and female rats treated with gonadal hormones. *J. Comp. Psychol., 34:*285, 1942.

10. Beach, F. A., and Holz-Tucker, A. M.: Effects of different concentrations of androgen upon sexual behavior in castrated male rats. *J. Comp. & Physiol. Psychol., 42:*433, 1949.

11. Beach, F. A. and Jordan, L.: Effects of sexual reinforcement upon the performance of male rats in a straight runway. *J. Comp. & Physiol. Psychol., 49:*105, 1956.

12. Goltz, F.: Der Hund ohne Grossshirn. *Pflüg. Arch. ges. Physiol., 51:*570, 1892.

13. Goltz, F.: Über den Einfluss des Nervensystems auf die Vorgänge während der Schwangerschaft und des Gebärakts. *Pflüg. Arch. ges. Physiol., 9:*552, 1874.

14. Bard, P.: Oestrual behavior in surviving decorticate cats. *Am. J. Physiol.*, *116*:4, 1936.
15. Beach, F. A., Zitrin, A., and Jaynes, J.: Neural mediation of mating in male cats. II. Contributions of the frontal cortex. *J. Exper. Zool.*, *130*:381, 1955.
16. Zitrin, A., Jaynes, J., and Beach, F. A.: Neural mediation of mating in male cats. III. Contributions of the occipital, parietal, and temporal cortex. *J. Comp. Neurol.*, *105*:111, 1956.
17. Beach, F. A., Zitrin, A., and Jaynes, J.: Neural mediation of mating in male cats. I. Effects of unilateral and bilateral removal of the neocortex. *J. Comp. & Physiol. Psychol.*, *49*:321, 1956.
18. Rosenblatt, J. S., and Aronson, L. R.: The decline of sexual behavior in male cats after castration with special reference to the role of prior sexual experience. *Behaviour*, *12*:285, 1958.
19. Gantt, W. A. H.: *Experimental Basis for Neurotic Behavior*. New York, Paul Hoeber, Inc., 1944.
20. Green, J. D., Clemente, C. D., and de Groot, J.: Rhinencephalic lesions and behavior in cats; an analysis of the Klüver-Bucy syndrome with particular reference to normal and abnormal sexual behavior. *J. Comp. Neurol.*, *108*:505, 1957.
21. Beach, F. A., and Zitrin, A.: Induction of mating activity in male cats. *Ann. New York Acad. Sc.*, *46*:42, 1945.
22. Kinsey, A. C., Pomeroy, W. B., Martin, C. E., and Gebhard, P. H.: *Sexual Behavior in the Human Female*. Philadelphia, W. B. Saunders Co., 1953.

VII

NEURONS AND NEUROSES

RALPH W. GERARD, M.D., PH.D.

M ANY years ago Lashley made a profound statement; he said, "Psychologists must choose whether to be vague or be wrong." In the field that we are engaged in examining at this symposium it is still, sadly, very far from being possible to be precise and correct at the same time. We are much in the position of the two opossum hunters, with one gun, one of whom had the shakes. After the sound man fired a number of times with no success, the other had a try. He held up the gun and the muzzle wobbled all over, but when he fired the opossum fell down. The first fellow grumbled, "No wonder! You covered the whole tree."

Dr. Goldfien this morning wisely worried about minds that were willing to reason in the absence of reliable facts. This is, indeed, a great source of danger; in fact, I have often argued the same way when speaking here. Conversely, though, we all recognize that, unless we are prepared to make a certain number of guesses, we won't know where to look for the crucial facts to prove, probably, that we are wrong. I am going to take the liberty today of giving you some of the pictures that I have been playing with; even though I am quite sure that they are wrong in detail and would not bet very big odds against their being wrong in totality. They do, however, enable me to put things together in a way that makes sense for me, and they will give you at least something to shoot at.

All living things are engaged in a perpetual tracking operation; each organism is concerned to ride two rails into the future, the rail of the expected and the rail of the desired; and most of life activities (not all) are concerned with bringing the expected into the realm of the desired by appropriate tracking correction maneuvers. When the organism is "on beam," so to speak, there is relative ease, contentment, a certain amount of exploration, play, somnolence; but sooner or later, and usually sooner, the organism gets off beam, something changes in the environment, and then occur the reverse kind of changes, increasing attention, anxiety, stress, in bringing about appropriate corrective maneuvers.

Clearly, the better the brain, the greater the projecience, the more things in the environment to which attention can be given, the sooner and more often will the organism become aware of a threatening divergence and the more will be the strain to correct it. The senses we have just heard about—in connection with Barcroft's embryo as the trigeminal gets to the snout, and in connection with arousal in the male when the various receptor mechanisms are intact—bring information in; but only as these signals have meaning to the organism, as several speakers have emphasized, does the stimulus constitute any kind of a threat or stress or, looking at it positively, cue to appropriate responsive behavior. In this sense, one can say: worry requires the cooperation of a worrier.

You will remember, perhaps, Kipling's lovely story of the two camels discussing their fellow beasts in relation to the Indian campaigns in which they were used. One said, "The elephant is a coward. He is not like the donkey, who willingly carries his burden into the line of battle." The second camel disagreed, "No; this is not a matter of cowardice at all. The donkey is a stupid animal and doesn't know what is going to happen to him. The elephant is wiser and understands what is involved in this, so he is afraid to go." "Well," said the first camel, "What about man, who is still wiser and none-the-less goes?" The second one shrugged his hump, "That's why man isn't an animal."

What, then, matters to an individual; and, of course, mattering usually does involve the emotions at some level? I will remind you of some things that you know well enough. As has been brought out in the last talk, and in earlier ones, much of what matters, of what can arouse emotional responses (with or without the emotions, depending on the part of the nervous system left intact) is inborn. This is essentially uniform for the particular species, is the result of racial experience and selection, and is something with which we are not now particularly concerned. Inborn "meaning" is represented in the basic material organization of the nervous system, its centers and tracts, and determines susceptibility to drugs and like general responses.

But in addition to such awareness or meaningfulness of stimuli, common to the race, there is for each individual his own particular experience in which certain meanings have come to be very important to him. I remind you of the experimental neuroses, such as the autonomic responses studied by Gantt. After each dog was given a varied shock experience, violent tachycardia or other cardiovascular responses developed when these animals were simply brought into the appropriate environment.

A comparable human case came to my attention a long while ago. A perfectly "normal" college freshman, being examined routinely in the health service, keeled over in a dead faint as he came down the line for examination of the heart sounds. The health physician finally showed, with the student's heart beat visible under a fluoroscope, that he could stand at the other end of the room and bring from behind his back such varied objects as tubes, cones, and cylinders with no effect; but when he brought out something that could clearly be identified as part of a stethoscope, the student's heart stopped. Unfortunately, no one sought out the antecedents of this response; but clearly here was a stimulus that had highly precise and highly dramatic meaning to this particular individual. Psychiatrists' experiences abound in reports of comparable cases; of women who show vicarious menstruation when certain material comes up in the course of psychoanalytic sessions, and so on and on. You have been told of the athletes who, perhaps not on an irreversible basis here, developed a vast outpouring of appropriate adrenal hormones under stress. Similar is the older work showing a great fall in eosinophils in the coach anxiously watching his team; he is responding to very meaningful emotionally stressful situations.

I have introduced the words "reversible" and "irreversible"; it is time to face this point more precisely. The situations that I mentioned are essentially irreversible residues of individual experience. I am sure I need not belabor the monist notion that Dr. Grinker espoused last night—as nearly all of us here do— that the organism is an entity and at any given moment faces the future as it then is, the only residue of its past being in terms of what it then is. What it is, might involve either some dynamic state or some morphological state. A dynamic state exists until some irreversible change has been produced, some morphologic change which endures even though the active process has subsided.

The one direct evidence for this sequence involving memory is offered by experiments done some years ago. Hamsters learned a maze, and were then either given electroshock, which certainly abolished dynamic reverberation in the brain, or were cooled down to about 5° C., which did the same thing. When they emerged from this experience, they had full memory of what they had learned; so the memory was not dynamic but included a structural residue. But some time (actually many minutes) is required to produce this fixation, time which differs under different conditions and may differ even in parts of the nervous system.

What happens with these traces of experience is that some kind of material difference is left behind in the nervous system; either in the individual neurons or in the organization of these neurons vis-à-vis one another. This is the engram or whatever word you prefer for it. But this is no longer quite so vague a thing as when the term was coined simply to epitomize our lack of knowledge. For example, when one occipital lobe is removed from a rat and the other occipital lobe removed two weeks later, animals retain their ability to use patterned vision in guiding behavior. If, however, during the interval between removal of the first occipital lobe and removal of the second one, the animals are kept completely in the dark, they lose entirely their ability to make visual discriminations. Clearly, during this two weeks' interval new patterns are being laid down in the brain under the influence of visual experience, and obviously being laid down in relation to pre-existing ones which serve as a kind of neuronal template. When this further experience is prevented and all the template is removed, then patterned vision is lost.

Or, take the cases of imprinting of which we hear so much. The experiments of Liddell with a young kid and its mother seem of this type. If the newborn kid is removed from its mother for as short a time as half an hour and then brought back, the two never quite make a go of it. The mother doesn't really accept this animal as her very own offspring, the kid is partly rejected, and even a year later such an animal is underweight and fragile, indeed many of them die, although it is presumably being given all the normal immediate physical care. There is some failure to establish the normal neuronal patterns for interacting because of the separation.

Interesting experiments suggest that this may happen at lower levels. Unilateral loss of cerebellar connections gives an asymmetrical posture in the lower part of the body. If this is produced a few hours before a high spinal section, the postural asymmetries below the cut are not lost. Some trace has been left in the lower part of the neuraxis by the asymmetrical presence of impulses from the cerebellum, when the asymmetry existed only for a few hours. This bears out the older, well known experiments of removing one cortical hemisphere or one motor area. Such a dog circles toward the lesion, and continues to do so after the symmetrical region is removed after some days. Again, some irreversible change has been brought about.

The nature of this, and the mechanism of fixation, I cannot take time to discuss at any length. Suffice it to say that there is now strong evidence, from several kinds of experiment and on several kinds of organism, that there is a finite fixation period, already mentioned, between having an experience and having that experience leave an enduring memory. In the hamster experiments, for example, if electroshocks are given not twelve hours after an experience but one hour, there still is progressive learning; but if the interval is reduced to fifteen minutes or less there is great and progressive impairing of learning. So, between the experience and the shock—which stops whatever is going on in the brain—there are minutes during which an irreversible fixing occurs. It is very tempting, and there are other reasons to support this, to believe that during this period nerve impulses are vigorously reverberating in neuron assemblies or loops. With repetitive activity there are cumulative changes in the basic properties of neurons—in their afterpotentials, their chemical reactions, their electrolyte exchange, and, associated with these, in synaptic transmissivity—and it is a fairly easy step from the reversible changes of a few impulses traveling, to an irreversible trace produced by long trains of them—as sufficient rain wears a path for itself in the land surface.

This process can be further studied. The temperature coefficient for fixation is the same as that for the speed of conduction of nerve impulses, nearly three; well in the range of chemical reactions in general. Fixation is slowed not only by cooling but by certain drugs, such as the barbiturates; as Miss Rabe and I have just reported. Morrell told a recent international symposium of some fascinating results along comparable lines. It is possible, in rabbits and other animals, to produce continued activity, leading to actual convulsive discharges, by putting alumina cream or other irritant on a particular region of one cortex, say the motor area. If this is left undisturbed for a week, then the equivalent region in the crossed cortex also becomes ictal; its threshold for electrical stimulation goes way down and it shows spontaneous convulsive discharges. Indeed, it can even be cut entirely from the surrounding and subjacent cortex and still give convulsive seizures. Of course, no alumina cream ever got near this particular bit of brain; actually, if either the discrete path through the corpus callosum or the diffuse one from below is not intact, this sensitization does not come about. Here one has almost a paradigm of the development of what, without too much poetry, could be called a "microneurosis"; as a result of overactivation maintained for a sufficient time, basic changes have developed in the involved neurons and abnormal behavior responses to normal inputs have come about.

The Morrell group has some evidence, still tentative, that the ribonucleic acid in these conditioned ictal cells is increased—which really gets to the molecular level that Dr. Elkes asked for this morning. Other dramatic work, by McConnell, Thompson, and others, points in the same direction. They taught the ordinary flatworm a conditioned response, to a sound or a light, with the unconditioned stimulus a shock. The flatworm turns in a way which is highly characteristic. The trained animals are then cut in two between the head and tail ends. Flatworms don't mind this too much; the head regenerates a new tail and the tail regenerates a new head. After some weeks for this regenerative process, the head-origin flatworms and the tail-origin flatworms were tested for their memory of the learned performance. There are few if any neurons in the tail (though this is perhaps still moot), but the tail remembered rather better than the head did!

If these results are held up, and careful controls are being done on them, we are indeed thrown back to the molecular level for memory traces. And there are interesting speculations in several quarters on how the particular pattern of incoming messages reaching a neuron impart their information to polynucleotides that are being synthesized. (Neurons are rather unique in that there is a rapid and continuous turnover of cell material, perhaps as much as three times a day, so that on a template of existing nucleic acids, new ones are continuously being formed.) If the pattern of electric fields set up by nerve impulses could somehow lead to a changed pattern of laying down the mononucleotides or folding the whole chain, this would be a start on the molecular basis of memory fixation.

All this is fine; but we don't require it as yet to make sense of the problem of memory at the neuron level. We have heard here and elsewhere of the great increase in knowledge of how the environment acts upon the organism as a whole, and of how the organism as a whole interacts with its contained nervous system, through the hormonal and vascular and autonomic mechanisms presented so well. There is further evidence for certain parts within the nervous system which are specially concerned with emotional as compared to conative behavior, the discrete and the diffuse nervous systems already introduced. One might be tempted, in fact, in view of its concern with affect, the emotional tone setting in which the particular content patterns that come through the discrete system are modulated, to call the diffuse system, in contrast to the discrete one, the "indiscreet" system. One can, then, simplifying egregiously, emphasize the difference, on the one hand, between the particular patterns, laid down as a result of individual experience and giving the specific content to awareness for a given individual, the conative and ideational aspects with or without affect; and, on the other hand, the general tone or setting or level or awareness in which the patterns of experience manifest themselves.

We are ready now to consider the basic question which must underlie all relations of behavior and experience, normal and neurotic: the question of just what is happening to neurons. These other questions are wrappings to it; whether coming from the molecular level or from the body level, what matters is whether neurons do or do not discharge. With our present knowledge of the nervous system, of behavior, and of consciousness we must assume a pretty close 1:1 relation between the activity of neurons in some form or other and the experiences and behaviors associated with them. So how do neurons come into and out of activity? I have indicated how the patterns are established; how are they activated or quieted?

A neuron becomes active when the amount of excitation impinging upon it is greater than that needed to bring the excitation level above its threshold; so neurons will become active either if their thresholds are lowered or if the bombardment of nerve impulses on them is increased. I am presenting this in the positive sense; obviously, taking away inhibition—either removing inhibitory impulses or substances that raise thresholds—would have the same effect. Two sorts of mechanism for lowering neuron thresholds have been put before you by the previous speakers: impulses from the diffuse system (reticular formation, limbic system, and the rest), and appropriate change in the chemical milieu. This latter can involve salt changes; increased potassium or lowered calcium raises irritability, but mainly involves the hormones, and the one most likely to deserve attention in this connection is certainly epinephrine.

I am bothered by the fact Dr. Kety gave us this morning, that tracer techniques show epinephrine does not enter the nervous system, and wonder if the present findings are decisive. Contrary evidence includes: his own finding that epinephrine but not norepinephrine greatly increases the oxygen consumption of brain; the experience of many of us that epinephrine or norepinephrine, infused into nurses or interns in small quantities, can give cardiovascular responses without anxiety, in the case of norepinephrine, or anxiety without peripheral effects, in the case of epinephrine; and our observation that epinephrine injected into the hypothalamus of the cat lowers thresholds for knee jerks and for motor responses, with a secondary wave due to the release of epinephrine from the adrenals. I shall wait to see, therefore, whether the new finding is one of those ugly facts that kills beautiful theories.

In any event, here are two well known mechanisms, whatever the particular chemical or chemicals may be and whatever the particular nerve tracts from whatever part of the old or new brain may be; two ways in which neuron thresholds can be modulated, in the present case reduced so as to make neurons more responsive.

What, next, about the barrage on them? Ordinarily, with habituated behavior—with well-established adaptive responses to the kind of stimuli with which the organism has been and continues to be presented—there is an automatic reflex kind of response, that mostly does not even evoke consciousness. You find yourself scratching an itch without being aware that you had an itch or were scratching. If, however, this routine response does not eliminate the disturbance (we are back on tracking, something in the environment has displaced the equilibrium), impulses continue to pour in through the afferent paths. Then the well-known physiological mechanisms of activation come into play. Summation, first, leads to, second, irradiation; impulses cross more and more synapses and reach additional neurons. Third, they probably begin to reverberate and, if they go on long enough, fourth, will produce fixations and lead to engrams, which may be healthy or may be unhealthy depending on the condition.

The electrophysiological evidence for such a wide lighting up of neurons throughout the upper nervous system is now well established. An animal with electrodes scattered about its cortex and lower parts of the brain, given a new kind of stimulus or a new problem to solve, develops widespread, vigorous electrical activity. As it learns the answers, so to speak, most of this disappears and there remain quite localized electrical concomitants of the problem solving. If the animal makes a mistake or the problem is now shifted, all light up again. All this fits the picture I have been developing.

Since time is pressing, I shall make here just one conclusion from this and refer to other publications for further implications. I like to think of a physiological neuron reserve in the brain. The more anatomical neurons there are, of course, the greater the potential physiological neuron reserve; but they are not all active, or even available, all the time. As new problems present for solution, summation and irradiation engage new neurons, and the conscious level rises from somnolence or passiveness to alertness, to vigilance, and on to anxiety. Performance is progressively improved during such arousal. If the process goes beyond some optimum—not really known—presumably reverberation occupies many neurons, and these assemblies can no longer be mobilized for flexible performance in the whole neuron "army." With certain parts of the brain preoccupied with reverberating activity, behavior now becomes less effective and shows a stereotyped or stenotic character. When a person gets too anxious, he stops exploring new paths and reiterates the same ineffectual response. And, with still more neurons locking, the whole performance breaks down and behavior becomes completely unadaptive.

So, first by simple radiation and, secondarily, by drawing in, as emergency mechanisms, the diffuse system and the endocrine or other chemical sensitizers, there occurs an initial waxing and, if the process goes too far, a later waning of the physiological neuron population in use. Such a neural picture fits rather nicely the stages of performance under increasing anxiety; it fits also the breakdown of performance with progressive age or under certain drugs; and a number of the thought disturbances shown by schizophrenics also fit the notion of a diminishing physiological neuron reserve.

The solution of mental illness is, to a large extent, not altering the initial engrams; this is, as you see, very difficult. Certainly to alter a patterned engram, an appropriately patterned psychotherapeutic approach rather than a generalized chemotherapeutic one gives more hope of a precision correction. The solution often is in cutting down the discrepancy between the desired and the expected by decreasing one's expectations, pulling in one's horns, getting old, giving up. This is also a type of homeostatic adjustment that helps adjust to illness and aging and other indignities of living. What neural mechanisms are involved in the value system and in the degree of aspiration insisted upon, and what neural changes enable an individual to give up his system when the pain becomes too great because of this discrepancy, will make a topic for some future symposium. At present, the answers remain in the domain of dynamic psychiatry.

The reader is referred to two recent articles for full bibliographic citations:

REFERENCES

1. Gerard, R. W.: Neurophysiology: an integration. In *Handbook of Neurophysiology*. (In press.)
2. Gerard, R. W.: The fixing of experience. In *Brain Mechanisms and Learning*. J. F. Delafresnaye, Ed., Springfield, Thomas; Oxford, England, Blackwell Scientific Publications Ltd. (In press.)

DISCUSSION

Dr. Karl H. Pribram: I would like to pause with you for a moment to ask a question. Appropriately perhaps, for this is the moment of the ego: between sex and neurosis just covered, and the inevitable death session that is to follow. What are we talking about? No one so far has dared ask, what is it that

we are talking about when we discuss physiology of emotions?
I feel like getting off the platform and letting you answer this
for yourselves during the pause.

To try to tie together some of the things that Drs. Frank
Beach and Ralph Gerard talked about, I shall present to you
some other experiments that may shed some light. The things
they talked about, of course, do have relevance to the physiology
of emotions—and point up two separable aspects of the problem.

First, consider a series of experiments performed by Schachter[1]
at the University of Minnesota. Human subjects were injected
with adrenalin just prior to taking some fairly complicated and
difficult paper and pencil tests. The subjects didn't take these
tests alone, however; there were three or four other people in
the room awaiting the same examination. The experimental subject
did not know these other people. These other people taking the
examination were primed ahead of time to display one of two
moods. Either they were to make light of the examination and
act as if they didn't care very much about what happened, joke
about it and in general take the examination in a rather pleasant
fashion; or they were primed to make it look tough, to grumble
and grouse, to kick up a lot of fuss about being examined and
even to make some nasty comments about the experimenter.
Compared with the controls the experimental subjects interpreted
the altered feeling produced by the adrenalin in one of two
ways: either they felt high and euphoric or they felt low, depressed. and even paranoid. The interpretation depended on the
social environment in which the experimental subjects found
themselves.

Perhaps then, we want to call socially determined behavior
of this sort, our reaction to social factors, "emotion." Is this the
"emotion" that we've been talking about, the kind that Dr. Beach
and Dr. Gerard have been discussing this afternoon? If so, a
large component of emotion is obviously determined by some
"cognitive mechanism." Is this the "expectation" Dr. Gerard
mentioned, the sexual "forethought" of male organisms Dr. Beach
discussed? In other words, is "emotion" determined not only
by such excitability or activating factors as were discussed this

morning and which we might call "affective" but also by this more "cognitive" component?

Let's look at some animal experiments to see whether there is any support for this dichotomous notion of what the "emotional process" might be all about. An experiment done in Dr. Magoun's laboratory by Green, Clemente, and de Groot,[2] tested sexual behavior in cats following amygdalectomy. There were reports in the literature that sexual behavior after amygdalectomy is enhanced markedly both in primates and in carnivores. "Hyper-sexuality" was the label attached to this phenomenon. Other laboratories failed to confirm the finding that hypersexuality followed amygdalectomy. Green, Clemente, and deGroot decided to study some normal cats before interpreting their observations on the animals with brain operations. Surprisingly, they found that normal cats were pretty sexy creatures and they saw very little difference in the degree of sexuality between the normal and the operated animals. There was an important difference, however; the normal cat, especially the male, did not display his sexuality everywhere and with everything. He restricted his sexual behavior to those situations which cats consider "proper." The operated animals on the other hand, did not restrict their sexuality to these situations: thus the interpretation that they were "hypersexual."

The same sort of analysis applies to the effects of amygdalectomy on other kinds of social behavior. A monkey is tamed rather dramatically following amygdalectomy; in fact, of the operations made on the endbrain, this one is about as dramatic as any in changing the temperament of the animal. But if one makes the operation in an animal which is a part of a stable social hierarchy, then one finds that an animal becomes either tame or *more* aggressive. Which effect results depends not only on the total social hierarchical structure, but especially and crucially on the aggressivity of the animal just below the operated subject in the dominance hierarchy. What happens to the operated subject in his interactions apparently determines not only his social position but the temperament he displays in similar situations wherever they may occur.

The Physiology of Emotions

How do these socially determined effects on the emotional process fit with the kind of thing that was discussed this morning? Dr. Gerard put it very nicely when he said that there are two tracks which guide life: the desired and the expected. Perhaps the chemical mechanisms that were talked about this morning give origin to the desired; and perhaps this isn't as complicated as we intellectualizing male animals make it out to be. Dr. Elkes gave us some excellent suggestions as to how to go about finding this simplicity. And perhaps if the social factors are treated separately, the chemical factors can be studied in purer culture. And by studying the neural mechanisms that are involved when each set of factors is operative some confluence in "mechanism" should be attained.

So if we are to talk about emotion at all perhaps we can distinguish two types of neural mechanism involved. One of them has to do with the moment-to-moment reactivity of the organism, which we might call its "affect" or disposition. This reactivity mechanism appears to be very sensitive to its immediate *chemical* environment. The other is a longer range mechanism: it is composed of inborn or learned restrictions imposed on the reactive mechanism. These more "cognitive" functions, perhaps cortical, determine the complexities of the process. Do these complexities tend to distort the affective process? And are these distortions the ones that not only get in the way of moment-to-moment gratifications in our daily lives, but also of obtaining simple answers in experimental laboratories? If so, clear separation of the two types of mechanism by experimental design should prove fruitful to investigators interested in the subject matter discussed this morning as well as to those whose interests are more closely allied to the program material of this afternoon's session.

REFERENCES

1. Schachter, Stanley: Personal communication, 1959.
2. Green, J. D., Clemente, C. D., and de Groot, J.: Rhinencephalic lesions and behavior in cats; an analysis of the Klüver-Bucy syndrome with special reference to normal and abnormal sexual behavior. *J. Comp. Neurol.*, *108*:505, 1957.

VIII

THE PSYCHOPHYSIOLOGY OF DEATH

PANEL DISCUSSION

Moderator
DAVID McK. RIOCH, M.D.

Participants

Life-Influencing Interactions
CHARLES C. HERBERT, M.D.
and
NANCY E. MEAD, M.A.

Possible Endocrine and Neuroendocrine Contributions
MAURICE S. GOLDSTEIN, M.D.

Symbolic Behavior Relative to Illness and the Threat of Death
EDWIN A. WEINSTEIN, M.D.

INTRODUCTION

*D*R. *David McK. Rioch:* No general definition of the subject—the psychophysiology of death—will be attempted, since the concept of "the psyche" is commonly defined in subjective terms and the definition of "death" in multicellular organisms is necessarily arbitrary, dependent on the purposes or values inherent in the particular situation. Attention will be paid, rather, to a variety of behavioral phenomena—autonomic, endocrine, symbolic, and social communicative—which appear to be related to one or other aspects of death.

Since the time of Claude Bernard it has become increasingly clear that life in warm-blooded animals is dependent on maintaining the internal milieu constantly within narrow limits. The general principle that the body resists deviations from the "normal" values and that following displacement there is a tendency to return to "normal" values has been more concretely formulated by Cannon in his principle of homeostasis. Cannon further demonstrated that in a wide variety of situations the sympathetic division of the autonomic nervous system played an important or major role in homeostasis. Particular emphasis has been placed on the effector organs and their nervous control and on those patterns of interaction with the environment in which a sudden requirement for a high rate of energy output would probably be useful—attack, escape, seizing of prey, and so forth. Since these patterns of behavior are included in the group from which the concepts of "emotional" and of "the emotions" have been inferred, the relationships of "emotions" to homeostasis and to health and illness have been provided with an experimentally derived broad conceptual frame of reference which is now widely accepted.

That the mechanisms subserving homeostasis may not so act, but may lead to exhaustion or death by their normal activity in certain situations has long been known. For example, Norman Freeman[1] in Cannon's laboratory found that sympathectomized decorticate cats, stimulated to continuous struggle by partial restraint of movement, lived longer than similarly treated decorticate cats with their sympathetic system intact. Brouha, Cannon, and Dill[2] showed that sympathectomized dogs could maintain a level of intense work on a treadmill as efficiently as normal dogs and even more efficiently than some normal dogs which were initially excited. Thus, it would appear that for prolonged energy output increased sympathetic activity may lead to decreased efficiency or death. A wide variety of studies on athletes conducted by Dr. D. B. Dill and others in the Department of Industrial Physiology at Harvard provided confirmatory evidence. It was further shown that maximum physical efficiency could only be attained by long and careful training. In other words, the mechanisms subserving homeostasis are not inherently or innately efficient or adequate. There is a range of environmental situations in which they are more or less effective and with training they can be very effective in limited areas. Beyond this range the same mechanisms can lead to responses of no demonstrable use or even to exhaustion and death. Another example may be taken from the field of temperature control. If the body temperature — due to high environmental temperature and humidity — rises to 106° F. or above and the organism is brought quickly into a cool environment, quite normal shivering may supervene and raise the body temperature to a more rapidly lethal level. In contrast, it is well known in the arctic that sitting down to rest, wearing adequate arctic clothing, at low temperatures in the open, may lead to sleep and freezing with no shivering at all. These two results are presumably to be explained by characteristics of the cutaneous cold receptors failing to provide central mechanisms with information relevant to more than their immediate environment. Further examples of incongruous hyper- and hypoactivity of autonomic systems under physical stress may be found in the reports on battle casualties in Korea by the Surgical Research Team under Captain John M. Howard, MC USAR.[3]

Although a great deal of work has been done on visceral sensory endings and on "reflexes" and more complex patterns of behavior evoked from their stimulation, very little in the way of general principles can be formulated. It would appear that we are dealing with a considerable variety of separate circuits subserving different functions, but we know little as to what data on intrasomatic events are being transmitted to the central nervous system and still less as to how these data are processed. As with other central nervous mechanisms, the input is largely determined by the preceding or concomitant output and thus both are influenced by the transaction in which the organism is engaged and by its course. For example, Wolf and Wolff[4] found the sensitivity of the gastric mucosa varied with the state of the mucosal vascular bed at the time. It is, therefore, not surprising that many different types of reaction have been observed in which viscerovisceral "reflexes," "emotion" attitudes and other (sometimes seemingly unique) patterns of behavior seem to have been responsible for morbidity and/or mortality. Thus, every physician of experience can recall anecdotal data of death or recovery contrary to all reasonable expectations. In view of the large number of variables involved, it is also not surprising that classification of syndromes and determination of the sequence of events has proceeded slowly, or that theoretical formulations follow current fashions rather than being based on operational measures.

Where the environmental contingencies vary more widely than the range for which the so-called innate homeostatic mechanisms can compensate, manipulation of the environment can be used to extend the range. Drawing a sharp distinction between the automatic mechanisms (including the autonomic) and those requiring discrimination and anticipatory use of manipulation of the environment is not feasible. Use of environmental factors and of posture for temperature control is necessary for many animals in hot, humid climates. Finding, acquiring, or selecting necessary food, water, and salt obviously requires behavior classed as cognitive, though the maintenance of homeostasis is dependent on it. Dr. Curt P. Richter, of the Henry Phipps Psychiatric Clinic, has studied these functions extensively in rats. His findings comparing the performance of the laboratory strain and the wild strain of the same species (Norwegian grey rat) have demonstrated not only the remarkable capacities of this species for manipulating the environment to control body temperature, selecting food to meet bodily needs, and performing other basically homeostatic functions, but also the disastrous effects on adequate data processing of the hyperalert state that is shown by the wild strain in the strange environment of the laboratory.

Richter's experimental results provide confirmation of field observations on other mammals and on man. The so-called "adaptation" of human beings to arctic, desert, tropical jungle, and other environments, as well as to rapid changes in altitude is mainly a function of organization of behavior appropriate to the situation, with particular attention to its anticipated temporal structure. In this regard it is important to note that the central nervous system directs the interaction of the organism with the environment on the basis of information received from a very large variety of sensory organs (transducers), the functions of most of which are not yet known. The control of the input from these transducers—for example, by behavior we call "attention" (cf. Galambos, et al.[5])—and the different ways in which messages from these organs may be processed, together with the obvious limitations in the rate at which the nervous system can process data, lead to certain inevitable results. Errors of admitting too much or irrelevant data, errors of excluding relevant data, or errors of incorrect processing of data increase the probability of further errors.

This problem is in part solved in mammals by preferred patterns of behavior (precomputed answers) with, as it were, "built-in" *anticipatory* operations which are functions of previous experience. In so far as the anticipatory symbolic behavior (which prepares the organism for the probable responses of the environment) correctly anticipated the course of the transaction, performance may well improve. When the organism is unprepared for the environmental response, the problem of central reorganization of function to meet the "unexpected" course of events may be disruptive. The subjective phenomena of euphoria and dysphoria which seem to accompany these increasingly adequate or increasingly inadequate central nervous functions are probably the basis for the concepts of the "love" versus "death instincts," "security" versus "anxiety," "living" versus the "catastrophic reaction," and so forth, of dynamic psychiatry.

The behavior commonly called "emotional" may thus be characterized as follows: a preferred transaction of short duration, leading to a sharply defined consummatory act or state, utilizing limited criteria for processing information as relevant or irrelevant and controlled during its course by little other than its course of approach to its consummation. "Emotional" patterns of behavior (excepting very rare instances) are limited, rigid, and stereotyped and thus, when the person is engaged in some secure, more or less contemplative transaction, these patterns are subject to extensive symbolic elaboration. "Emotional" behavior is fortuitously effective or disastrous depending on the long term course of behavioral events. Thus, occasionally one finds people who are able to use emotional patterns as subtransactions in the course of certain highly complex social transactions of considerable duration. The great majority of people, however, are dependent on the social system to maintain temporal continuity and stability. For this great majority, therefore, what may be called "having the right emotions" is of paramount importance since only so can social communication in the cultural group continue reliably under conditions of stress.

The great specialization of man's central nervous system, permitting an unprecedented degree of variability and modifiability of behavior, requires the learning of informal as well as formal social roles and of the rules governing the use of these roles, transition from one role to another, punishment and atonement for misuse of roles, and so forth (cf. Money *et al.*[6]). The relationship of the "emotional" behavioral roles to the problem of death is therefore of interest. Under reasonably secure conditions, when there is time to review hopes, desires, accomplishments, relationships with other persons, and so forth, in our culture the preferred communication is of avoidance—by escape or attack—of death with expressions of fear, resentment, anxiety, or other feelings. When, however, a member of our culture is in a critically dangerous situation, his overt behavior and concomitant autonomic and subjective activity are usually quite different. In *Men Against Fire* Brigadier General S. L. A. Marshall (Retired)[7] has provided extensive evidence that the danger of the battlefield is not death or mutilation. Men can "steel themselves" to face these. The danger is its "lonesomeness"— that is, a man cannot tolerate being *left alone*, without commitment to his fellows or of them to him and without the support of their concurrence in his actions. It is at this point that one finds the difference between formulable "emotional" patterns of behavior, and panic, with loss of communication and continuity. In contrast with the combat situation is the highly controlled, stereotyped, socially organized situation of execution for a capital crime. Faced with inevitable death, a large proportion of people approach the final moment punctiliously playing the social role assigned by the social group of their choosing, and without the manifestations of disturbance which death as the prime danger of life might be expected to evoke. A great deal of attention was paid to this phenomenon at the time of the French Revolution, but with the growth of the humanitarian ideals and their incorporation in our cultural legal system interest in the variability of human behavior in approaching its terminal act has become more limited.

It seems fairly clear that if an organism goes into a state of panic (in which activity is directed by the immediately current input, with loss of temporal structure) the maintenance of life is jeopardized. The question arises, however, as to whether there are organized, limited, and stereotyped, "emotional" patterns of behavior which may or may not be "useful" under certain circumstances, but which facilitate lethal intrasomatic activity under other circumstances. The answer to this question would seem to be definitely in the affirmative.

Despite the favored position of sea sickness in humorous anecdotes the fact remains that it represents a condition with high morbidity and some mortality. The dilatation of the stomach and concomitant nausea, sweating, fast pulse, sense of dysphoria, and weakness resulting from vestibular stimulation have no "useful purpose" that can be recognized. The problem is raised as to whether, in order to obtain a system adequately sensitive to coordinate postural and visceral activity, it is necessary—in teleological terms—to run the risk of the results of its overactivity in a certain proportion of the population. If such is the case we would be dealing with a situation resembling the anticipatory hyperactivity of the sympathetic "emergency" mechanisms, which under certain circumstances proves deleterious. It is of interest to note, however, the contrast between the small demonstrable role of the vestibular system under ordinary conditions in primates and its flagrant symptomatology when unbalanced or overactive input results from disease or from environmental contingencies. The concern with "weightlessness" for man in space illustrates the significance of this system.

Apart from the phenomenon of hyperactivity of particular

nervous mechanisms as noted above, several studies in recent
years have directed attention to more general changes in the
functional organization of the nervous system resulting in
inadequate performance, disease, or death. For example, clinical
investigations using interview methods on hospitalized patients
have suggested that the initial symptoms of a wide variety of
diseases are temporally associated with subjective changes which
may be interpreted as depression following the real or symbolic
loss of or separation from an important person (Schmale[8]). In
laboratory experimental studies it has been found that peptic
ulcers and other lesions of the gastrointestinal tract may develop
in monkeys during investigations on their behavior and emotional
reactions under psychological stress.[9] Further studies of these
phenomena show that pronounced changes (rise) in the levels
of blood pepsinogen and adrenal cortical steroids occur following
and not during the period of stress. It thus appears that the
durations of the alternating stress and rest periods are more
important than the severity of the stress in precipitating these
organic changes.

Probably the most dramatic evidence for the importance to
the lethal results of certain central nervous activity is provided
by Richter's experiments on rats.[10] In the course of studies on
survival swimming in water at different temperatures, Dr. Richter
found that occasional rats would swim to the bottom of the
tank and die within minutes instead of maintaining themselves
at the surface for hours, as did the majority. This phenomenon
was further investigated both in domesticated (laboratory strain)
Norway rats and in recently trapped, wild Norway rats. The
situation was made more threatening to the rat by clipping off
the whiskers just before immersion in the water. This procedure
was previously shown to deprive the rat of important orienting
information. Under these conditions all of the wild rats died
promptly, but only about one out of four of the domesticated
strain died.

The cause of death was investigated and it was found that
at autopsy the lungs did not contain water and the rats had not
drowned. Suspecting overactivity of the sympathetic system, the

investigators measured the heart rate by taking the electrocardiogram through wires attached to the chest wall. This showed a very high rate initially with sudden slowing and cardiac arrest at the time of death. It thus appeared that death was due to massive vagal discharge. The use of drugs confirmed these conclusions.

In order to clarify the basis for this reaction, the separate steps in the method of transferring the rat from the cage to the swimming tank were analyzed. The difficult problem of handling wild rats had been systematized previously. A black cloth cone on a frame fitted the door of the cage and the rat would run into this when the sliding door was opened. Retreat was prevented by pressing the cone closed with a rod behind the rat which was then grasped through the cloth, with thumb and forefinger holding the head gently, but firmly, and with the rat's body held in the palm of the hand. The cloth cone could then be peeled back, exposing the head, legs, and front of the animal. The whiskers were clipped and the rat dropped into the water. It was found that some rats died in the course of these manipulations before being put in the tank, but that the most threatening parts of the maneuvers were the restraint of being held and the immersion in the water.

Dr. Richter concluded from his observations that the reaction of the rat was not that of "fight or flight"—the reactions commonly associated with hyperactivity of the sympathetic-adrenal systems—but appeared more as hopelessness, in response to the confinement and restraint, against which there was no defense. It was as though there was nothing to do and the rat would "give up." This concept was tested as follows. The rat was repeatedly caught and held and then returned to the cage or dropped quickly into the water, taken out and returned to the cage. After several repetitions of these maneuvers the complete process was carried out, including clipping the whiskers. Rats so trained did not die, but struggled and when immersed in the water swam as well as or better than domesticated Norway rats. It would therefore appear certain that death was due to a central nervous response to the situation and that this response could be modified by experience. Pretreatment with chlorpromazine also protected some of the wild rats, though not as consistently as the conditioning method.

The importance of these findings lies in the fact that they have brought into the laboratory a syndrome—psychologically induced disorientation, weakness, and death—which resembles much anecdotal evidence of phenomena seen in other animals and in man under unusual and fortunately rare circumstances. The question as to whether increasing or massive vagal discharge may also represent the mechanism of so-called "voodoo death" remains to be demonstrated. One may note that at least it is not contrary to the small amount of data available on the latter. Other vascular and hormonal mechanisms, however, must also be considered in such cases and also in the deaths described of certain prisoners of war[11] and of persons in concentration camps,[12] as well as in the extreme weakness noted in troops under certain circumstances, such as at Omaha Beach.

In conclusion one may say that the functional organization of the central nervous system changes with experience so that the interaction of the organism with the accustomed environment tends to improve to a considerable extent through more adequate, anticipatory, symbolic behavior. In unusual or extreme circumstances, failure to process data from the environment correctly in relation to the temporal as well as the spatial contingencies may lead to behavior (precomputed output) which increases the problem of maintaining the interaction within tolerable limits and so leads to disease or death. In the human of necessity most of the precomputed answers to situational problems are in the form of models represented by conventional clichés, folklore, and myths. In novel and extreme situations, therefore, human verbal behavior can be interpreted only on the basis of careful observation of actual performance in the social setting in which it occurs.

REFERENCES

1. Freeman, Norman E.: Decrease in blood volume after prolonged hyperactivity of the sympathetic nervous system. *Am. J. Physiol.*, *103*:185, 1933.

2. Brouha, L., Cannon, W. B., and Dill, D. B.: The heart rate of the sympathectomized dog in rest and exercise. *J. Physiol.*, *87:* 345, 1936.

3. Howard, John M., Editor: *Battle Casualties in Korea.* Vol. I, II, III, and IV, Army Medical Service Graduate School, Walter Reed Army Medical Center, Washington, D. C., Gov't. Printing Office, 1955.

4. Wolf, Stewart G., and Wolff, Harold G.: *Human Gastric Function: An Experimental Study of a Man and His Stomach*, 2nd ed. London, Oxford Univ. Press, 1947.

5. Galambos, Robert, Sheatz, Guy, and Vernier, Vernon G.; Electrophysiological correlates of a conditioned response in cats. *Science, 123:*376, 1956.

6. Money, John, Hampson, Joan G., and Hampson, John L.: Imprinting and the establishment of gender role. *A.M.A. Arch. Neurol. & Psychiat.*, 77:333, 1957.

7. Marshall, S. L. A.: *Men Against Fire.* Washington, Combat Forces Press. New York, William Morrow & Co., 1947.

8. Schmale, Arthur H., Jr.: Relationship of separation and depression to disease. I. A report on a hospitalized medical population. *Psychosom. Med.*, 20:259, 1958.

9. Porter, R. W., Brady, J. V., Conrad, D., Mason, J. W., Galambos, R., and Rioch, D. McK.: Some experimental observations on gastrointestinal lesions in behaviorally conditioned monkeys. *Psychosom. Med.*, 20:379, 1958.

10. Richter, Curt P.: On the phenomenon of sudden death in animals and man. *Psychosom. Med.*, 19:191, 1957.

11. Nardini, J. E.: Survival factors in American prisoners of war of the Japanese. *Am. J. Psychiat.*, 109:241, 1952.

12. Tas, J.: Psychical disorders among inmates of concentration camps and repatriates. *Psychiat. Quart.*, 25:679, 1951.

LIFE-INFLUENCING INTERACTIONS

Dr. Charles C. Herbert: The internist is concerned with the understanding and care of people. He views the sick as maladjusted people attempting to adapt to the challenge of the stimuli in their environment. These stimuli may be social, cultural, psychological, organic, or inorganic. People adapt to these stimuli by shielding themselves from them, by depending on or

strengthening their inherited defenses, or by changing their
environment. In the dying patient, the maladjustment may be
either specific but crucial, or multiple and significantly
accumulative.

Theoretically, in any one dying person's maladjustment, the
psychological components may be either merely concomitant,
or primarily causative, or contributive. We have sought in the
literature evidence to support any or all of these theoretical
possibilities. We look hopefully for case reports where clinical,
physiological, pathological, and psychocultural observations were
recorded. Disappointingly few have been discovered. Mostly the
sociologist, psychiatrist, pathologist or other medical specialist
would perceive or describe only those features of the total
phenomenon pertinent to his special interest or training. Unusual
opportunities for a multidisciplined study were wasted. The
recounting of a number of examples to reinforce this point as
well as for their anecdotal worth seems justified.

"A celebrated physician, author of a work on the effects of
the imagination, was permitted to try an astonishing experiment
on a criminal who had been condemned to death. The prisoner,
an assassin of distinguished rank, was advised that, in order that
his family might be spared the further disgrace of a public hang-
ing, permission had been obtained to bleed him to death within
the prison walls. After being told, 'Your dissolution will be
gradual and free from pain,' he willingly acquiesced to the plan.
Full preparations having been made, he was blindfolded, led to a
room and strapped onto a table near each corner of which was
a vessel containing water, so contrived that it could drip gently
into basins. The skin overlying the blood vessels of the four
extremities was then scratched, and the contents of the vessels
were released. Hearing the flow of water, the prisoner believed
that his blood was escaping; by degrees he became weaker and
weaker, which, seemingly, was confirmed by the conversation
of the physicians carried on in lower and lower tones. Finally,
the silence was absolute except for the sound of the dripping
water, and that too died out gradually. 'Although possessed of
a strong constitution, [the prisoner] fainted and died, without
the loss of a drop of blood. "[1]

". . . a soldier . . . was acting as a servant . . . in East India [and was] reprimanded severely [by his officer] for something he thought he had done. The soldier denied the allegation and was very much hurt. He asked him to retract what he said. He declined to do so.

"The fellow went out into the desert, squatted down in the sand, covered his head, and died . . . no evidence of any cause [of death was found] other than mortification."[2]

The noted surgeon[2] recounting this story added that a number of his doctor missionary friends have corroborated the phenomenon among certain tribes—that where the feelings of an individual are badly hurt he will go out into the desert, squat down, pull his robe over his head and die promptly without any other known cause for it. This surgeon was personally so convinced that there is something to emotional or psychic shock that he refused to operate on the patient who said in effect, "All right, I'll be operated on, but I will die"—and he does die.

The striking similarities of some of the reports suggest either that they are merely variations of a theme or substantiations of a syndrome.

"A young Negro on a journey lodged in a friend's house for the night. The friend had prepared for their breakfast a wild hen, a food strictly banned by a rule which must be inviolably observed by the immature. The young fellow demanded whether it was indeed a wild hen, and when the host answered 'No,' he ate of it heartily and proceeded on his way. A few years later, when the two met again, the old friend asked the younger man if he would eat a wild hen. He answered that he had been solemnly charged by a wizard not to eat that food. Thereupon the host began to laugh and asked him why he refused it now after having eaten it at his table before. On hearing this news the Negro immediately began to tremble, so greatly was he possessed by fear, and in less than twenty-four hours was dead."[3]

"During my first stay, a tragic taboo affair happened at Samkita. A boy at the Mission school there had as his taboo that he must not eat plantains, and must even be careful not to eat any food out of a cooking-pot in which plantains had been cooked immediately before. One day his schoolfellows told him that he had eaten fish from a pot in which there had been remains of plantain. He was immediately seized with cramp and died after a few hours. A missionary who was present gave me an account of this perplexing affair.

"And I have heard quite reliable accounts of other cases which ended with the death of the person who was burdened with the taboo."[4a]

"An assistant was hated by the students of a college. They condemned him in a joking manner to death, carrying out the ceremony in a serious manner. The assistant was held with his head on the chopping block, eyes bandaged, while one student made the noise of a swinging axe, another dropped a warm, wet cloth on his neck. The assistant died instantly."[5]

A man was "reprieved, after his head had been laid on the block and the fatal axe was about to fall. The reprieve came too late — the anticipation of death had arrested the action of the heart."[6a]

The ability to willfully influence the cardiac rate is ascribed to a Colonel Townsend who

"possessed the remarkable faculty of throwing himself into a trance at pleasure. The heart ceased apparently to throb at his bidding, respirations seemed at an end, his whole frame assumed the icy chill and rigidity of death, while his face became colourless and shrunk, and his eyes fixed, glazed and ghastly; even his mind ceased to manifest itself, for during the trance it was as utterly devoid of consciousness as his body of animation. In this state he would remain for hours, when these singular phenomena wore away and he returned to his usual condition."[6b]

Doctors Cheyne and Baynard and a Mr. Skrine reported in detail the phenomena on the day of the Colonel's demise. They first felt his pulse which was

". . . 'distinct, though small and thready, and his heart had its usual beating. He composed himself on his back and lay in a still posture for some time. I found his pulse sink gradually, till at last I could not feel any by the most exact and nice touch.

Dr. Baynard could not feel the least motion in his breast nor Mr. Skrine see the least soil of breath on the bright mirror he held to his mouth; then each of us by turns examined his arm, heart and breath, but could not by the nicest scrutiny discover the least symptom of life in him.' They waited some time and the body continuing in the same state, were about to leave, under the impression that the Colonel was actually dead when a slight motion in his body reassured them; upon examination, the pulse and heart were found again in action, and he gradually restored himself. His death-like state lasted half an hour, and recurred at nine in the morning, after which he transacted business with his attorney, and quickly expired at six o'clock in the afternoon; and the body when examined presented, with the exception of the right kidney, no signs of disease."[6c]

A physician[7] reports of his patient, a young man in training to be a champion boxer:

"He was a magnificent specimen of manhood and was not lacking in courage. Two days before his expected match he had a slight hemorrhage from the lungs. . . . There were rales in the chest, but I could find nothing marked. I told him to stay in bed and keep quiet. As I was leaving the house the mother told me that the parish priest was coming and suggested that, as the young man had not been attending to his church duties for some time, it would be well for the priest to see him. Fearing that the patient might be frightened by the advent of the priest or his attempt to perform in a religious way, I cautioned the mother, but, nevertheless, the priest saw the boy and ill-advisedly, in my opinion, administered the last rites. This was at 3 p.m. The young man was terribly alarmed, and by 6 p.m. he was dead. The cause of death I do not know. As I had seen him about 10 a.m. the case was one in which a coroner's examination was required. The coroner pronounced his death due to the hemorrhage, but as this involved only a small amount of bleeding, I have always thought that, as the boy was afraid to die, aggravated fear when he was shrived so unexpectedly caused his death."[7]

From Mount Sinai Hospital, New York, a psychiatrist[8] reports, without further details, a female patient who while under general anesthesia for a leg amputation suffered cardiac arrest on the operating table, which required life saving intervention. She stated afterwards, "I made up my mind not to come out of the anesthesia. I didn't want to live with my foot cut off."

An anesthesiologist[9] reports the instances of a ten year old boy and a forty-nine year old woman who died without adequate cause on the operating table with negative necropsy findings and who were unusually apprehensive prior to operation.

A pathologist[10] reports at least one hundred forty carefully investigated cases in which the cause of death was not disclosed by autopsy out of a total of seven hundred to eight hundred cases of sudden and unexpected deaths of young soldiers during World War II. In eight instances death was preceded by an acute psychotic disturbance manifested by violent emotional and physical agitation.

A psychiatrist[11] in the Spanish War of 1936-39 reported on about one hundred people with the syndrome of malignant anxiety, only three of whom survived. They

"showed anguish and perplexity rather than fear or excitement; they remained sitting or lying without any spontaneous activity, barely answered questions, except with 'Yes' or 'No,' could scarcely concentrate, but were not very confused; the pulse rate was permanently above 120, and the respirations were 40 or more (in two cases . . . 75 per minute). At first sight they looked like overstrained dogs. The tendon reflexes were much increased; the cutaneous reflexes were exaggerated but were more variable. No focal symptoms were observed. The urine was concentrated and extremely acid, with a peculiar smell.

"At the end of the first week, sometimes even earlier, the temperature rose very quickly and the general state became worse. The tongue became ulcerated and blackish; the skin was slightly jaundiced, the abdomen tympanitic. The mental state changed: although the anguish remained, the patient became restless and exhibited an increasing number of automatic movements; carphologia appeared; subsultus tendinum and facial spasms, specially roused by touch, were observed." In almost all the cases signs of hypocalcemia were observed. "Death occurred after three or four days . . . there was no delirium . . . the cerebrospinal fluid was normal except that the pressure was always increased and no focal symptoms were observed. In some, post-mortem examination showed swelling of the brain and even haemorrhages."[11]

In the three patients treated symptomatically and with intravenous hypertonic solutions of $MgSO_4$ and small repeated doses of lobeline catamnesia disappeared and after one month they were discharged completely recovered.[11]

Predisposing conditions appeared to be: (1) a previous lability of the sympathetic system, (2) a sudden severe mental shock experienced in conditions of physical exhaustion due to lack of food, fatigue, sleeplessness, etc., (3) more than one day before starting sedative treatment.[11]

Four hundred and three cases of the acute exhaustion syndrome in excited psychotic patients are reported[12] as being characterized clinically by antemortem excitement, hyperpyrexia (100° to 110° F.), tachycardia, hypotension, and sudden cardiac arrest after two days to two weeks. Consistent autopsy findings have been limited to general visceral and cerebral vascular congestion with petechiae, small hemorrhages, and occasionally cloudy swelling of cortical and subcortical neurons.

A detailed report[13] of unexplained death in a thirty-six year old male coexistent with death wishes demonstrated many of the features of the acute exhaustion syndrome. Of special interest was the phenomenon the patient demonstrated of lying extremely rigid, at times with moderate opisthotonos, conscious, staring toward the ceiling, holding his mouth wide open, and volitionally breathing with rapid, shallow inspirations. He held his thoracic cage in taut overdistension, "obviously struggling with all the energy at his command to retain as much air in his lungs as possible."

Peculiar respiratory features are described[4b] also in Africans who, burdened by their taboos, are seized by terrible spasms accompanied by breathing difficulties—"near to suffocation." An instance is described of a woman whose delusion was overcome through persuasion and who recovered, but fatal cases are reported.

Asphyxiation due to sudden cataleptic rigidity of the muscles of breathing is offered[14] as an explanation for death from "silent panic":

"... in the spring of 1943" a London "shelter was overcrowded, there was a bomb explosion nearby; the electric power failed, lights went out and somebody stumbled on the stairs. There was a sudden upheaval of tremendous fear in the pitch dark; no yelling or crying were heard. When first aid arrived nearly 200 of the 600 people were dead. Post mortems revealed no significant anatomical changes in the victims.

"... In the shelter, in the midst of dark unknown, the terrified notion that all would die killed 200 people.

"The characteristics of the silent panic are silence, darkness and utter fear. It is as if in this communicationless moment of utter despair a telepathic transfer of the most primitive sham-death reaction has taken place, with all its physical consequences."[14]

Sham death or tonic immobility has been studied[15] in many creatures (lizard, bird, hen, guinea pig, young dog, cat, sheep, fox, opossum, ape). It has been simulated in man by having him bend forward from the waist through an angle of 90°, place his hands on his abdomen, take a deep breath, and then permit himself to be thrown violently backwards through 180° by a man on either side. His skeletal muscles contract vigorously and a state of pronounced immobility lasting a few seconds may result. The onset in the lizard is usually characterized by a period of deep gasping respirations, followed by a gradual decrease in amplitude and frequency of respiratory movements until breathing is hardly perceptible, by heightened tone of the leg muscles, and by a certain degree of nonreactivity to the environment, although the eyes frequently remain open and alert. Immobility may persist for seconds or several hours, its duration being a problem distinct from its production. The onset is considered to be "induced by 'shock' to the centers of reflex tonus causing promiscuous discharge of these centers with accompanying inhibition of the higher centers." Of special interest is the effect of the injection of small amounts of epinephrine above a threshold value to produce a prolongation of the duration of the tonic immobility by an amount which is a logarithmic function of the dose.[15]

An accident that occurred during the second World War[16] strikingly illustrates the somatic effect of emotion. Three qualified deep-sea divers were confined underwater for totals of seventy-five, seventy-three, and seventeen hours. Only one of the three was affected by panic. He alone died.

The first diver, twenty-six years of age, was tunneling through the mud beneath the wrecked hull of a sunken LST, in order to pass a cable to the second. The hull shifted and he was incarcerated beneath mud and wreckage, unable to move or to see, at a depth of fifty-five feet. Rescue was complicated by wreckage, debris, and the entrapment of two other divers. Air supply and telephone remained intact. "Throughout, the patient retained a clear sensorium and remained calm and cooperative . . . he succeeded in dozing periodically. He would awake with a start and anxiously await reassurance that rescue efforts were proceeding according to plan. . . . The diver's spirited courage was a source of inspiration to those working above. The known physical hardships of his predicament — no food or water for 3 days; . . . necessity to urinate in his diving suit — were dwarfed by the psychic implications of his helplessness." When examined within minutes after rescue, he was "an alert, calm, cooperative individual who appeared physically exhausted." After supportive therapy he felt reasonably well, and showed no serious physical, neurologic, or psychic sequelae.

The second diver, twenty-four years of age, was tunneling to meet the first when the wreckage shifted . . . "he was thrown off balance and immobilized in the mud in a horizontal position. A large metal plate pressed against his anterior thorax. He struggled futilely to change his position . . . became excited and progressively more frantic. Attempts to reassure and calm him via the telephone did not succeed. He exhausted himself trying to move a limb, change his position, and free himself. Respirations heard over the 'phone, were rapid, grunting, and labored." Within less than eleven hours "he was disoriented and irrational." About an hour later, "telephonic contact was lost. Respirations were no longer audible." When the dead man was brought to the surface, approximately seventy-five hours after the descent had been begun, his diving suit and helmet were intact and air containing. His control valve was open and an adequate air supply was present. The body was that of "a very well-developed white male." Although putrefaction impeded post-mortem examination, the examiners found evidence of acute, extreme pulmonary congestion, and considered the diagnosis of asphyxiation; but why asphyxiation should have occurred was not clear, since a constant air supply had been maintained throughout the rescue operation and the air compressors were keyed for maximum output. One hypothesis was that the dyspneic and hyperpneic respirations might have led to a toxic concentration of carbon dioxide within the helmet. The author, remarking that the man may have been "scared to death," observed that even a highly stable person might succumb to anxiety in circumstances so extreme.

The third diver, a thirty-six year old man who descended voluntarily in an effort to rescue the other two, was pinned by a metal plate across his thigh as the wreckage shifted further, and worked loose from this confinement only to find his air line fouled. He was trapped for seventeen hours at a depth of forty-five feet. During the entire time he remained calm and cooperative, and survived without residual ill effect.

All of the three men involved had been thoroughly trained and were experienced in their hazardous work. The circumstances that entrapped them were virtually alike. We are thus presented with, in effect, a "controlled experiment" in the effects of emotion. The death of the one man that succumbed to his emotional response to incarceration may be a dramatic example of the potentially lethal power of fear.

These reports seem to lend support to the hypothesis that psychological factors may so challenge some people's adaptive mechanisms that the resulting disintegration proceeds to total maladjustment and death.

Of greater interest to me, and I suggest, of greater importance, if I correctly relate them to our modern medical practices, are the reports from the more "primitive" cultures. For from them I gained an increased awareness of the therapeutic and detrimental effects of our cultural attitudes towards disease and death.

Hopefully, after much controlled study, we can decrease some of the nontherapeutic stimuli.

"Dr. S. M. Lambert[3] of the Western Pacific Health Services of the Rockefeller Foundation wrote to" Dr. Walter B. Cannon "that on several occasions he had seen evidence of death from fear. In one case there was a startling recovery. At a Mission at Mona Mona in North Queensland were many native converts, but on the outskirts of the Mission was a group of nonconverts including one Nebo, a famous witch doctor. The chief helper of the missionary was Rob, a native who had been converted. When Dr. Lambert arrived at the Mission he learned that Rob was in distress and that the missionary wanted him examined. Dr. Lambert made the examination, and found no fever, no complaint of pain, no symptoms or signs of disease. He was impressed, however, by the obvious indications that Rob was seriously ill and extremely weak. From the missionary he learned that Rob had had a bone pointed at him by Nebo and was convinced that in consequence he must die. Thereupon Dr. Lambert and the missionary went for Nebo, threatened him sharply that his supply of food would be shut off if anything happened to Rob and that he and his people would be driven away from the Mission. At once Nebo agreed to go with them to see Rob. He leaned over Rob's bed and told the sick man that it was all a mistake, a mere joke — indeed, that he had not pointed a bone at him at all. The relief, Dr. Lambert testifies, was almost instantaneous; that evening Rob was back at work, quite happy again, and in full possession of his physical strength."[3]

Dr. P. S. Clarke, working on the sugar plantations of North Queensland, reported to Dr. Lambert[3]

"One day a Kanaka came to his hospital and told him he would die in a few days because a spell had been put upon him and nothing could be done to counteract it. The man had been known by Dr. Clarke for some time. He was given a very thorough examination, including an examination of the stool and the urine. All was found normal, but as he lay in bed he gradually grew weaker. Dr. Clarke called upon the foreman of the Kanakas to come to the hospital to give the man assurance, but on reaching the foot of the bed, the foreman leaned over, looked at the patient, and then turned to Dr. Clarke saying, 'Yes, doctor, close up him he die' (i.e., he is nearly dead). The next day, at 11 o'clock in the morning, he ceased to live. A postmortem examination revealed nothing that could in any way account for the fatal outcome."[3]

Dr. Herbert Basedow[3] presents "a vivid picture of the first horrifying effect of bone pointing on the ignorant, superstitious and credulous natives, and the later more calm acceptance of their mortal fate:

" 'The man who discovers that he is being boned by any enemy is, indeed, a pitiable sight. He stands aghast, with his eyes staring at the treacherous pointer, and with his hands lifted as though to ward off the lethal medium, which he imagines is pouring into his body. His cheeks blanch and his eyes become glassy and the expression of his face becomes horribly distorted. . . . He attempts to shriek but usually the sound chokes in his throat, and all that one might see is froth at his mouth. His body begins to tremble and the muscles twist involuntarily. He sways backwards and falls to the ground, and after a short time appears to be in a swoon; but soon after he writhes as if in mortal agony, and, covering his face with his hands, begins to moan. After a while he becomes very composed and crawls to his hut. From this time onwards he sickens and frets, refusing to eat and keeping aloof from the daily affairs of the tribe. Unless help is forthcoming in the shape of a counter-charm administered by the hands of the Nangarri, or medicine-man, his death is only a matter of a comparatively short time. If the coming of the medicine-man is opportune he might be saved.'

"The Nangarri, when persuaded to exercise his powers, goes through an elaborate ceremony and finally steps toward the awestricken relatives, holding in his fingers a small article — a stick, a bone, a pebble, or a talon — which, he avows, he has taken from the 'boned' man and which was the cause of the affliction. And now, since it is removed, the victim has nothing to fear. The effect, Dr. Basedow declares, is astounding. The victim, until that moment far on the road to death, raises his head and gazes in wonderment at the object held by the medicine-man. He even lifts himself into a sitting position and calls for water to drink. The crisis is passed, and the recovery is speedy and complete. Without the Nangarri's intervention the boned fellow, according to Dr. Basedow, would certainly have fretted himself to death. The implicit faith which a native cherishes in the magical powers of his tribal magician is said to result in cures which exceed anything recorded by the faith-healing disciples of more cultured communities."[3]

Dr. Stewart Wolf and others[17a] observed in the Southwest Pacific, on Goodenough Island, d'Entrecasteaux Group, British New Guinea, a patient who was approximately thirty years old, and in the Australian Regimental Hospital under the care of Sgt. Hill of the Australian military service.

". . . the patient was admitted with the complaint that 'pouri-pouri' had been made 'against' him, indicating that a potion had been mixed and incantations recited by a person of recognized competence and power.

"The implications were that the victim had broken a taboo and he was made aware of the fact that he had been subjected to 'pouri-pouri.' He knew, in short, that he was regarded as dead by his fellow tribesmen. On being ignored, rejected, and excommunicated, and after a period of panic, he had become listless, apathetic, and inert. He expressed at no time a desire to live, and acted as though convinced that his end was near. He had taken to his pallet and refused food and water before being brought to the hospital.

"The examination on admission revealed an individual who appeared slightly above his estimated age. He exhibited splenomegaly, skin yaws, and slight arterial hypertension. Although he did not appear severely ill, his state varied between one of frank depression and apathy, without terror, and remaining silent and more or less immobile. His pulse rate was 65, his heart was slightly enlarged, and x-rays of his chest were not contributory. His blood pressure subsequently was within normal range or slightly elevated. His past history revealed that he probably had had malaria, dysentery, and yaws.

"He showed no interest in the attention of the physicians. A successful attempt was made to get an anti-potion from his tribe and this was brought to his bedside, with assurance that his health would return. For a short time he partook slightly of the mixture presented to him, but then rejected it. The anti-potion remained at his side, untouched. He became increasingly apathetic, seemed detached and resigned, barely moved, and his bed covers remained undisturbed for hours. His skin and mouth were dry. His urine contained a slight amount of albumin and had a high specific gravity. He was seen to pass no excreta after the first few days.

"He received penicillin, arsenicals, and digitalis. No one came to see him and he interested himself in no other patients. On the ninth day after admission he was found dead in bed.

"Autopsy revealed cirrhosis of the liver, splenomegaly, and widespread arteriosclerosis. Also, amyloidosis of the spleen, kidneys, pancreas, and liver was revealed on histological examination. No immediate cause of death was discovered. The likelihood is that the death was due to rejection of fluids, brought about by psychological reactions to tribal rejection."[17a]

Among the primitive aborigines of the Northern Territory of Australia the "white" magician (medicine man) is little different as a social personality from the other members of his clan except that he is recognized as having a special power. He is sought by the relatives of a sick man to diagnose the illness and either to restore him to normal participation in the group or to pronounce his death sentence.

"The medicine man then helps organize and direct the community's attitude toward the sick man. . . . He examines his patient. . . . If he diagnoses the case as curable and removes the cause, he reestablishes the individual's equilibrium, making him believe he can once more participate in his usual manner in the group. He can do this because he organizes group attitude, since the belief in the curative power of this ritual unifies the point of view of all the members."[18a]

If the sick man is pronounced incurable, the social group demonstrates two definite movements, in the process of which black magic becomes effective on the victim.

"In the first movement the community contracts; all the victim's kin withdraw their sustaining support — everyone in his whole community, i.e., all his kin, completely change their attitudes and place him in a new category. He is seen no longer as an ordinary living being like all the other people, but as an abnormal person who is more nearly in the realm of the sacred and taboo. This movement of withdrawal by the society means that his place in the general social fabric has been taken away from him so that he now stands in an entirely different relationship to all of his kin, his clan, and the general tribal grouping. The organization of his social life has collapsed, and he is alone and isolated.

"The second movement of the group is its return toward the victim under the integrating force of the mourning rite. The 'half dead' man whose soul is in that dangerous position to the community of being neither sacred nor profane must be removed by ritual from any contact with his community; and its purpose now as an organized group with its ceremonial leader, a close relative of the victim's, is finally to cut him off entirely from the ordinary world and ultimately place him in his proper position in the sacred totemic world, that of the dead. The victim, on his part, reciprocates this feeling, behaving in the manner of his totem, with which he attempts to identify himself. The mourning rite is truly a *rite de passage*. The effect of this double movement, first away from the victim and then back with all the compulsive force of one of the most powerful rituals, is obviously drastic. An analogous situation in our society is hard to imagine. If all a man's near kin, his father, mother, brothers and sisters, wife, children, business associates, friends and all the other members of the society, should suddenly withdraw themselves because of some dramatic circumstance, refusing to take any attitude but one of taboo and looking at the man as one already dead, and then after some little time perform over him a sacred ceremony believed with certainty to guide him out of the land of the living into that of the dead, the enormous suggestive power of this twofold movement of the community after it has had its attitudes crystallized can be somewhat understood by ourselves.

"The magicians are the leaders who crystallize this group attitude. By the power of their rituals they organize social opinion and attitudes. . . . Both depend upon the group's participation to make their power effective. It is a group situation, not an individual one. . . . It is the power of the . . . community which integrates the total group, directed by the ceremonial leader . . . and it is the power of the . . . group which destroys a man under the guidance and leadership of its magicians."[18b]

Translated to our modern setting the members of the medical

The Physiology of Emotions

profession comprise the magicians who organize social opinion and attitudes toward sickness and health, and, with the theologians, toward death. With our emphasis on medical biophysical-chemical "science," have we not slighted or forgotten the therapeutic and nontherapeutic effects of the interpersonal, the cultural, and the environmental forces that impinge upon the sick patient and his family? Perhaps these important aspects of healing or killing would be more acceptable in terms of the social science of medicine.

In any event they are with us, we are responsible for them; so let us accept this fact and briefly look at them—and at ourselves.

It is generally accepted that resulting from the great medical advances over the past fifty years, the life expectancy at birth of the average white male has been significantly increased—in fact by 19.2 years to a total of 67.4 years. However, if we look at our advances in terms of the average increase in years of lifetime remaining among white males who managed to survive to age 45 in 1954, as compared to 1900, the number is 3.29 years. And if you lived to 65 years in 1954, medical advances increase your survival over a similarly fortunate male in 1900 by only 1.59 years (Table I). Now we are all grateful for little favors, but

TABLE 1. Average Remaining Lifetime in Years Among Whites

	Age 0		Age 20		Age 45		Age 65	
	M	F	M	F	M	F	M	F
1900	48.23	51.08	42.19	43.77	24.21	25.51	11.51	12.23
1954	67.4	73.6	50.3	55.9	27.5	32.2	13.1	15.7
Average increase	19.17	22.52	8.11	12.13	3.29	6.69	1.59	3.47

*From U. S. Bureau of Census. *Statistical Abstract of the United States: 1956.* Washington, D. C., 1956, p. 65.

I believe you will agree that there is still room for improvement. I submit that some improvement, especially in these age groups, will result through the recognition and utilization of present medical social science knowledge.

In recent times the care of major illnesses has shifted in setting from home to hospital. While undoubtedly advantageous to some of the seriously diseased or to those requiring major technical procedures, hospitalization is often for the therapist's convenience. His tasks have been greatly simplified, his responsibilities shared, diluted and shifted. Economic efficiencies have been realized by the concentration and coordination of facilities and services. However, efficiency should also be measured in terms of the therapeutic results and the serious patient liabilities that exist in the hospital setting. These hazards are physical, microbial, social, and emotional.

There is a growing awareness of this problem:

". . . the hospital embodies a social environment in which established procedures, distinctive attitudes, and structured interpersonal relationships exert powerful influences upon staff members and patients alike. It is also suspected that certain of the behavioral patterns, communicable attitudes, and stereotyped relationships, unless recognized and handled with care, can produce untold damage in treatment situations. Some of the personal relationships can become charged with exaggerated significance for the patient, so that his reactions, especially in the critical stages of his illness, may have decided effects upon his health and general welfare. The balance that exists, for example, in the patient's reactions to staff members between doubt and feelings of rejection, on the one hand, and trust and acceptance on the other, may often pivot on very fine points. And who can say just how often particular relationships tip the scales one way or the other in the course of an illness?"[17b]

For example, in a Helsinki University hospital[19] the incidence of sudden death in patients with myocardial infarctions of seven days' to six weeks' duration was 15% in association with ward rounds, compared to the expected chance incidence of 2 to 4%.

On the other hand, striking improvement of intractable disease in infants[20] and adults[21] has demonstrated the therapeutic aspects of the home care setting—ideally "efficient" both from financial and patient welfare viewpoints.

In San Francisco, while the death rate per 100,000 per year

has apparently changed surprisingly little over the past fifty years (Table II), the percentage of people dying in hospitals versus

TABLE II. San Francisco Death Rate — Per 100,000 Population

Year	Rate
1958	118
1949	126
1939	138
1929	127
1917	148
1909	129

*Compiled from statistics of the San Francisco County Department of Public Health, Division of Statistics.

their homes has risen from 38% to 68% in 1958 (Table III). In

TABLE III. Place of Death by Percentage in San Francisco

	Year	Total	At Home	In Hospital	Elsewhere
(September)	1959	668	32%	66%	2%
	1958	9375	27	68	5
	1949	9735	32	64	4
	1939	8746	34	62	4
	1929	7968	36	63	1
	1917	7294	47	51	2
	1909	6153	60	38	2

*Compiled from statistics of the San Francisco County Department of Public Health, Division of Statistics.

San Francisco, culturally speaking, the hospital is fast becoming the place to die, or perhaps, the place one is sent to die. A disturbing question is whether, with adequate medical home care, fewer people would die as early.

Of great interest is the fact that last month, in September 1959, 55% of the total deaths from heart disease versus 81% of the total deaths from cancer occurred in the hospital. Is heart disease a more culturally acceptable home condition?—at least to die from?

All but a few of one hundred patients[22] studied to determine the psychological impact of major surgical operations held irrational beliefs about the cause of their neoplastic disease. This finding casts doubt upon the contention that current dissemination of scientific knowledge restricts the acceptance of primitive beliefs regarding magical or supernatural causes of disease. Education influences the way a belief is expressed more than it determines the origin or nature of the belief. While cultural influences are recognized, the selection of any specific belief from the wide range of those possible is a function of the character structure of the believer. The authors presented the thesis that "a belief is a psychologically unique process which originates as a reality perception, is influenced by individual life experience, is integrated into a system of character defenses, and functions as a basis for action."[22]

Schweitzer[4c] states that what brought the natives to his African hospital was often "not so much the expectation of the care they would find as the need of being somewhere where the sinister forces of which they felt themselves the victims would be unable to operate." The sick were urged by their fellows to go to the hospital for fear that, if the patient died, their fellows might be suspected of having practiced fatal magic against him.

In our modern culture it would appear that people are expected to die in the hospitals where everything possible has been done for them, especially if attacked by the more threatening causally unknown or incurable diseases. The aged face the cultural conviction that for them useful life is over. When they become too big a nuisance many are forced to withdraw from the society they knew. Undoubtedly, this psychosocial clincher accounts in large measure for the shameful increase in the mortality rate among the aged who are abandoned to institutions, in contrast to the death rate among a comparable sample still functioning in their communities. Examination of these factors should prove an interesting and perhaps fruitful area of research.

Now let us look at our interpersonal relationships with patients.

This is about all the magician or primitive medicine man had to influence his patients—and the anecdotes indicate that it was potent enough to kill or cure.

Doctor-patient relationships are often initiated by chance, perpetuated through adjustments, or terminated through misunderstandings. They are rarely contracted for after the participants' deliberate consideration of their abilities to satisfy each other's needs. If we but knew enough to permit a therapeutically effective initial matching of patient and doctor based on a knowledge of the pertinent characteristics of each and the predictable dynamics of their interaction! A successful medical relationship is related to patient and doctor satisfaction, effective outcome as judged by appropriate unbiased means, and operational efficiency in terms of permitting the maximum quality of care with the monies and talents available. While the doctors in a medical community ideally are collectively responsible for satisfying the varying needs of its members, no one doctor is capable of satisfying the needs of all patients, and few the varying needs of any one. Doctors and patients are frequently unaware of their own or each other's needs. Almost invariably they are ignorant of the dynamics of their interaction.

Factors influencing the dynamics are pecuniary and nonpecuniary. For the doctor, the latter relate in part to the type of disease and the patient treated; in part to his investment in terms of time, convenience, and emotional involvement; and in part to the reward of increased esteem by self, colleagues, and patient. For the patient these relate to the servicing of his somatic, psychological, and social needs resulting in change in symptoms, signs, and levels of functioning and in his surviving or dying more or less comfortably.

Commonly as a result of the rigidity of their medical training and/or of their personalities, doctors try unsuccessfully to categorize their patients' complaints under the known disease entities and/or to influence them by orthodox techniques, and then may lose interest or become anxious. They either "refer for consultation" with or without return designated, dismiss with "reassurances," or continue to prescribe "symptomatically" until either the patient becomes resigned to failure or "shops" for help elsewhere. This cycle is often repeated with great expenditure of time, money, and delays in obtaining relief. If the patient's needs were understood, and a doctor with satisfying characteristics were available, a more therapeutically successful and efficient initial matching would be possible.

I have attempted to characterize doctors along an intuitively derived continuum. Some doctors may or may not be aware of psychosocial needs of their patients but they limit their activities to certain manifest organic or psychological disease entities and treat them in a prescriptive and "scientific" fashion along orthodox lines. Other doctors have equal factual knowledge but their professional behavior is determined by a genuine interest in their patients as fellow human beings. They treat them with respect and understanding or compassion and with varying amounts of their own personal involvement in the interrelationship. If they are unable to define their patients' psychosocial needs but only sense them, they nonetheless treat them intuitively as fully as they can. Any one doctor may be the preferable one for a specific patient, depending on the needs to be satisfied. As the needs of any one patient may vary from time to time so may the characteristics of the "best" doctor or combination of doctors.

The pertinence of expectations—the patient's and the doctor's—to the understanding of therapeutic effectiveness compels an initial attempt to define and control the specific effects of a few of the many different forms of expectation. These may be scrutinized in the areas of expectation: fulfilled or unfulfilled; realistic or unrealistic, conscious or unconscious, culturally acceptable or unacceptable, optimistic or incredulous, assessed in terms of:

Characteristics of doctors; role-playing versus genuine involvement.

Types of "disease" and their changing phases (organically demonstrable or nondemonstrable, symptomatic or asymptomatic, "labeled" or unlabeled, etiology known or unknown, acute or chronic, socially restricting or nonrestricting).

Therapy including type (medical, surgical, psychological),

goals (specific, symptomatic, supportive), at what price (in time, money, complications, discomfort).

Similar and different opinions of doctor and patient regarding their expectations permit a study of the dynamics of their interaction and of factors influencing therapeutic effectiveness.

People influence people, themselves and others, to live and die.

REFERENCES

1. Yawger, N. S.: Emotions as the cause of rapid and sudden death. *Arch. Neurol. & Psychiat.*, *36*:875, 1936.
2. Finney, J. M. T.: Discussion of papers on shock. *Ann. Surg.*, *100:* 746, 1934.
3. Cited by Cannon, W. B.: "Voodoo" death. *Psychosom. Med.*, *19:* 182, 1957.
4. *a* Schweitzer, Albert: *African Notebook*. Bloomington, Indiana; Indiana University Press, 1958, p. 58.
   b Ibid., p. 60.
   c Ibid., p. 82.
5. von Lerchenthal, E. Menninger: Death from psychic causes. *Bull. Menninger Clin.*, *12*:31, 1948.
6. *a* Tuke, D. H.: *Illustrations of the Influence of the Mind upon the Body*. Philadelphia, Henry C. Lea, 1873, p. 87.
   b Ibid., citing Macnish, Robert: *The Philosophy of Sleep*. 3rd ed., 1836, p. 231.
   c Ibid., citing Symonds, J. A.: *Miscellanies*. 1871, p. 160.
7. McConnell, J. W.: In Yawger, loc. cit.[1]
8. Kaufman, M. R., Franzblau, A. B., and Kairys, David. Emotional impact of ward rounds. *J. Mt. Sinai Hosp.*, *23*:782, 1956.
9. Cronkite, A. E.: Necropsy findings in patients dying on the operating room table. *Anesth. & Analg.*, *36*:19, 1957.
10. Moritz, A. R., and Zamcheck, N.: Sudden and unexpected deaths of young soldiers: diseases responsible for such deaths during World War II. *Arch. Path.*, *42*:459, 1946.
11. Mira, E.: Psychiatric experience in the Spanish War. *Brit. M. J.*, *1*:1217, 1939.
12. Shulack, N. R.: Exhaustion syndrome in excited psychotic patients. *Am. J. Psychiat.*, *102*:466, 1946.
13. Alexander, G. H.: An unexplained death coexistent with death-wishes. *Psychosom. Med.*, *5*:188, 1943.

14. Meerloo, J. A. M.: *Patterns of Panic*. New York, International Universities Press, Inc., 1950, p. 37.
15. Hoagland, H.: On the mechanism of tonic immobility in vertebrates. *J. Gen. Physiol., 11:*715, 1928.
16. Romney, S. L.: Underwater confinement: Report of three cases. *U. S. Naval M. Bull. 46:*1259, 1946.
17. *a* Cited by Simmons, L. W., and Wolff, H. G.: *Social Science in Medicine*. New York, Russell Sage Foundation, 1954, p. 94.
    b Ibid., p. 174.
18. *a* Warner, W. L.: *A Black Civilization; A Social Study of an Australian Tribe*. New York, Harper and Bros., 1958, p. 232.
    b Ibid., p. 241.
19. Järvinen, K. A. J.: Can ward rounds be a danger to patients with myocardial infarction? *Brit. M. J., 1:*318, 1955.
20. Bakwin, Harry: Psychogenic fever in infants. *Am. J. Dis. Child., 67:*176, 1944.
21. Rossman, I.: The reduction of anxiety in a home care setting. *J. Chron. Dis., 4:*527, 1956.
22. Bard, M., and Dyk, R. B.: The psychodynamic significance of beliefs regarding the cause of serious illness. *Psychoanalyt. Rev., 43:*146, 1956.

POSSIBLE ENDOCRINE AND
NEUROENDOCRINE CONTRIBUTIONS

Dr. Maurice S. Goldstein: In any thesis concerning major and relevant psychogenic contributions to death, considerable strength may be added to the arguments by revealing plausible functional and anatomical bases for such processes. In studies of the endocrinology, biochemistry, and physiology of stress, death is frequently employed as a most convenient and dramatic end-point in the experimental design. From the extensive literature concerned with reactions to stress, a considerable body of information can be and has been interpreted in terms of a pivotal role of the central nervous system in contributing to the success or ultimate failure of adaptation which constitutes death of the organism.

On the face of it, this attention to the nervous system appears to be at odds with the more general concern with the adrenal cortex in stress. Loss of the adrenal glands by disease processes, by surgical removal, or in experimental situations results in one of the sharpest curtailments known in the capacity of the individual to adapt and survive. By contrast, in the normal organism, an almost endless variety of situational changes of internal and external character serve as stimuli for the release of ACTH from the pituitary with its resultant stimulation of secretion of steroid hormones by the adrenal cortex and the concomitant wide range of adjustments which are effected in the face of changing environmental demands. So compelling are these observations of the role of the adrenal cortex in successful adaptation to stress that a unified system of stress response involving pituitary and adrenal gland has dominated our thinking for some decades. Indeed, the biochemical parameters of the pituitary-adrenal cortex response have, in many hands, been identified as equivalent to the total status of the individual with deliberate disregard of the many other events which are set in motion by the same stimulus of exposure to a stressful situation.

An almost single-minded concern with the response of a single system is as much a necessary aspect of the initial phases of investigation as the drive to establish a so-called controlled environment of the laboratory in which the external and internal milieu of the organism is reduced as closely as possible to some basal vegetative norm. At some point however, a retrospective effort must be made to place the information in a more realistic relationship to the actual, variable world of biology. And it is in a world of growth, of infection, of disease, of periodic fasting and thirsting, of violent or gentle or affectionate relationship to other individuals, of situations of fright and panic, of real and imagined problems, that the gross incompleteness of the pituitary-adrenal response as representing the central reaction to stress becomes most apparent.

These hormones of the adrenal cortex are correctly labeled "vital" in that their absence leads to profound dysfunction and even death. And yet, the adrenalectomized organism, given an environment free of the demands of food and water gathering, of changes in temperature, of problems involving shifts in behavior and so forth, lives out its life in normal, vegetative serenity in the laboratory cage. Adequate growth, maturity, and even reproduction can be readily effected in the absence of these organs of response to stress. The tissues of such an individual are certainly deprived and deficient in whatever molecular, biochemical, and enzymological role the steroid hormone plays. This profound deficiency, however, has no apparent meaning under generally restful conditions. It is only under conditions where almost any kind of adaptative behavior is elicited, which is considerable both in degree and in extent in time, that the profound deficiency of the animal becomes manifest with catastrophic end result.

Even though release of ACTH and increased adrenal steroids occur with virtually any kind of stressful stimulus, this additional hormone supply is not critical or even essential at the onset. Given a small, fixed, daily quotient of steroid, the adrenalectomized organism can respond fully and adequately to stresses. The hormone supply is fixed by daily dose while the responses to stress still occur in full range and character for many hours or even days. This "permissive" property of steroids demands the search and recognition of other more relevant variable physiological systems in stress.

The meaning of the stressful stimulus deserves careful re-examination. The adrenalectomized animal, deprived of the pituitary-adrenal cortex response, is by no means impassive in the face of a stressful situation. Cardiovascular, muscular, metabolic, and behavioral responses, which are unique both to this particular individual and to the nature of the stress applied, proceed despite the absence of the adrenal cortex. It is this array of heightened activities in the absence of adequate steroid hormone which leads to the failure of blood vessel and metabolic process that constitutes adrenal insufficiency and ultimate death. It is activation of these nonadrenal processes which brings forth the picture of steroid dependence. It is only rarely that the actual physical aspects of the stimulus applied are intrinsically damaging. Instead, it is the adaptive responses that the organism makes which constitute the potential and real damaging agent in most reactions to stress.

This is not a unique consideration in endocrinology and is remarkably similar to the rather vague conceptions of "endocrine imbalance" which characterized the thinking of clinicians of another generation. Given the precision of measurements denied these earlier workers, we must now characterize such conditions as diabetes mellitus as the relative or absolute absence of insulin in the presence of at least a normal and possibly hyperfunctioning pituitary; the syndrome of diabetes insipidus as being due to a failure of antidiuretic hormone production or response in the presence of adequate thyroid function; and so on. In much the same way we are forced to view the manifestations of sensitivity to stressful situations in the adrenal insufficient animal as depending upon the presence of an adequately functioning and even hyperactive nervous system.

The experimental evidence for such a view cannot here be presented in detail, but can best be demonstrated by definitive modification of the susceptibility to stress which characterizes the adrenal insufficient animal. A variety of procedures which interrupt the central nervous system responses to stimuli and the sympathetic nervous system outflow in particular will reduce or completely obviate the adrenalectomized organism's fatal response to stresses. Situations which lead to catastrophic vascular shock and metabolic failure in the adrenalectomized organism, fail to do so if the spinal cord is sectioned high in the thoracic region; if peripheral blocking agents such as dibenzyline or dibenamine are applied to interrupt tissue responses to epinephrine and norepinephrine; if tranquilizing agents and anesthetics are administered simultaneously and full dose.

In a somewhat parallel fashion, chronic and progressive adaptation to the administration of epinephrine or norepinephrine yields an animal which becomes relatively independent of the need for steroids and can sustain stress after adrenalectomy to a remarkable degree. By minimizing central nervous system responses in a dulling, relatively stress-free, controlled environment; by anatomically or pharmacologically, reducing the outflow of the nervous system to tissues; or by adapting tissues to ever-increasing exposure to the neurohumors of the central nervous system, the highly stress-sensitive condition which results from lack of adrenal cortical hormone is markedly diminished or completely obviated.

Are these considerations unique to the relatively rare condition of adrenal insufficiency? Or do they have some bearing on the general considerations of reaction to stress in the normal organism? There are at least two very suggestive areas of evidence which indicate that the high degree of central nervous system control of physiologic and metabolic functions is potentially dangerous in many situations.

The considerations outlined for adrenal cortical insufficiency are not unique to that hormone. While severe vitamin deficiencies are no longer a major medical consideration in this country, they show parallel behavior to adrenal steroids which has been recognized since the eighteenth century. It was noted very early that a diet deficient in fresh fruit and vegetables could be sustained for many years by the withdrawn members of religious orders and by the recluse, while a mere matter of months of the rigors of sailing a ship with its fatigue and cold would on the same deficient diet lead to the usually fatal hemorrhages and infections of scurvy. The biochemical investigations of experimental vitamin C deficiency and the investigations of the role of vitamin C have justified these earlier speculations. The vitamin disappears from blood and tissues in deficiency states without any manifestations for even months. Any severe stressful demands in this period will now elicit full symptomatic expression of the deficiency. ACTH is, if anything, protective and not causative. It is the heightened demands of adapting—constriction of blood vessels and the like—brought into play by nervous response to situational stimuli which leads to breakdown of vitamin C deficient small blood vessels. Similar experiences have been reported with other water soluble vitamins and constituents. In general, the metabolism of tissues at rest and under load differ qualitatively as well as quantitatively. Innervation constitutes the major and ubiquitous manner of driving tissues to increased activity or "load."

Further evidence for primary consideration of the nervous system in reactions to stress is pointed up by the remarkably similar pathological processes of death induced by excessive administration of epinephrine and norepinephrine in the intact animal as is seen in the spontaneous failure of the stressed adrenalectomized animal. Adrenal steroids afford a great range of successful tissue responses to the epinephrines beyond which additional steroids fail to provide further support or protection. Yet when one exceeds these limits in the normal steroid-protected animal by further and additional administration of the epinephrines, there is a similar vascular collapse and a loss of capillary integrity and responsiveness—the institution of a pernicious and self-perpetuating vascular shock which is seemingly the same process as seen in adrenal insufficiency but at a different quantitative level. The steroids extend successful tissue responsiveness to the impulses of the autonomic nervous system but not indefinitely and adrenal insufficiency is representative of the normal situation of limitation of response to the epinephrines but at a far lower level of autonomic nervous activity.

One can then view the organism's total response to stress as being built primarily about the responses of the central nervous system. This has relevance in terms of endocrinologic studies of both the deficient and the intact organism. And such a presentation can afford a number of points of actual or potential interaction of psychogenic influences, which is our major concern at this seminar. First, the quality of the stimulus that elicits a variety of directional and unique as well as nonspecific patterns of response can have great individual meaning. Once the major role of a stress stimulus is understood to influence internal responses rather than to interact physically and directly with tissues, a great deal of apparently conflicting experiences in stress studies can be resolved. The general long-standing human knowledge that prior experiences are of great significance and importance can be incorporated in our views of response to stress. Information derived through the special senses of sight, sound and touch and taste, can be given specific meaning by an individual and serve to set in motion, in whole or in part, complexes of reactions usually identified as responses to extensive traumatic experiences. Repeated and chronic exposure to a particular stimulus can lead to its exaggeration as an eliciting or exciting agent or to its marked or complete restriction as a stressful stimulus. The interpretation of the stimulus quality of a given situation or experience can be markedly modified thereby without any change in the physical properties of that stimulus.

The nature of the response when elicited from the nervous system can be dealt with under the artificially designated systems of study of somatic nervous system, autonomic nervous system, neuroendocrine or hypothalamic - pituitary - endocrine outflows. But in fact, the actual integrated responses of the nervous system with its preset thresholds, its internal unique and individual information, its external stimuli, and its continual monitoring of all manner of physiologic and metabolic functions is of course independent of our technological or historic divisions of outflow from the nervous system. The extent and character of involvement of the many body functions is subject to a variety of influences. The intrinsic species-specific norms of regulation, the so-called "homeostatic norms," do not represent critical adjustment of function to the present need, with rare exception. As a rule a very healthy margin of reserve is represented by the regulatory situation. Blood pressure is kept at a perfusion level in excess of the minimal needs of tissues. Blood sugar level is maintained considerably above the concentration necessary to effect adequate entry of sugar. Oxygen level is maintained far above the critical requirements of diffusion into tissues to supply their needs, and so on. The shifts in response to many stressful situations represent the same exaggerated over-response built into the organism as baseline levels which err generously on the side of overproduction and over-response and keep clear of the dangers of insufficient service. We lack the necessary terminology to counter the temptation to deal with these measurements teleologically as "anticipatory" settings of reactions. This is largely balanced by the objective observations that the levels of resting regulation as well as the temporary new norms which characterize the changes in response to stress do occur in a direction of over-reaction when compared with the critical needs of the processes which these regulated functions subserve. Prior experience, early handling, present status can all modify these regulated norms in one direction or the other.

Beyond the organized outflow of regulating information from

the central nervous system lies the metabolic status of the peripheral tissues. The healthy or the diseased state of such tissues; the adequacy or the deficiency of their many internal components as well as external constellation of hormones, nutritional elements and so forth; the tissue adaptation or "training" which follows chronic exposure to almost any agent or influence, all play a role in the actual tissue response to nervous influences. In turn, the feedback of information from the peripheral tissues, from chemoreceptors, proprioreceptors, baroreceptors, and from metabolites forms a continuous internal source of modifying influences on the nervous system.

There are no compelling patterns of response in such a broader and more total view of reaction to stressful situations. Particular elements may be brought into action. Spontaneously or by deliberate design, one can impart to a given stimulus a capacity to elicit ACTH with its concomitant increase in circulating adrenal cortical steroids. This can be and has been accomplished without a more extensive and generalized involvement of mobilization of other tissue functions. In the same fashion, it is possible to see an excessive mobilization of cardiac action. The heart may be driven to excessive rates of contraction not as part of an appropriately integrated mobilization of cardiovascular function but independently of and indeed despite the internal information that increased return of blood to the heart is not occurring. Such isolated tachycardias may be meaningful in terms of the misinterpretation of some stimulus either external or internal but quite misleading in terms of the physiological status of the individual. A heart that beats rapidly in the face of increased return of blood is serving a highly successful physiological adaptation. One that beats excessively in response to some unique and individual central nervous interpretation without increased venous return can actually impair the functional output of blood by encroaching upon the time required for filling and lead to the cardiac insufficiency seen in paroxysmal tachycardia. Tachycardia is an essential quality of an adaptive cardiovascular system. Tachycardia, out of physiological context, as it were, is potentially damaging and destructive.

In brief and in summary, studies of regulation of endocrines and metabolism are leading to a progressive appreciation of the role of the central nervous system. As the pituitary was recognized to exert control of thyroid, adrenal, and gonads, the pituitary, in turn, is now seen to be firmly and extensively controlled by the hypothalamus. The entire functional organization of the brain can be brought to bear on the regulation or disruption of these major endocrine functions. In this manner, our appreciation of endocrinology is paralleling our understanding of the profound imposition of nervous regulation on cardiovascular, pulmonary, renal, and gastrointestinal systems.

The rapidity and ranges of responses and the progressive freedom from the more fixed physical restrictions of the environment seen in lower animals is unquestionably accomplished in the higher mammals by yielding endocrine, metabolic, and physiologic control to nervous regulation. This great potential has its price, however. The very complexity and sensitivity of the nervous system; the presetting of basic regulations to what appear to be anticipatory goals of regulation as opposed to immediate critical needs of physiologic functions; the ability to modify the entire process at almost any point, expose the organization to many possibilities of physiologically disproportionate and inadequate arrangements. Shifting responses from the physical and chemical properties of the stimulus to the central nervous interpretation of the meaning of the stimulus has afforded a new order of flexible adaptability on the one hand, but potential and destructive misinterpretation on the other.

BIBLIOGRAPHY

Goldstein, M. S., and Ramey, E. R.: Non-endocrine aspects of stress. *Perspectives Biol. & Med., 1:*33, 1957.

Levine, S., Alpert, M., and Lewis, G. W.: Differential maturation of an adrenal response to cold stress in rats manipulated in infancy. *J. Comp. & Physiol. Psychol., 51:*774, 1958.

Levine, S., and Otis, L. S.: The effects of handling before and after weaning on the resistance of albino rats to later deprivation. *Canad. J. Psychol., 12:*103, 1958.

Meiklejohn, A. P.: The physiology and biochemistry of ascorbic acid. *Vitamins & Hormones 11:*61, 1952.

Ramey, E. R., and Goldstein, M. S.: The adrenal cortex and the sympathetic nervous system. *Physiol. Rev.*, *37*:155, 1957.

Sayers, George: The adrenal cortex and homeostatis. *Physiol. Rev.*, *30*:241, 1950.

SYMBOLIC BEHAVIOR RELATIVE TO ILLNESS
AND THE THREAT OF DEATH

Dr. Edwin A. Weinstein: This paper deals with some of the changes in symbolic behavior or language that serve as means of adaptation to the stress associated with serious illness and the threat of death. It will also consider the adaptive functions of the idea of death itself much as Aristotle conceived of the function of tragedy as causing a catharsis of the emotion of fear through the imitation of some deed of suffering or horror.

The material is taken from studies of patients with major incapacities associated with brain damage who have been studied in successive stages of recovery of function with concomitant changes in the level of symbolic organization. The ideas derived from these data will be supplemented by observations of men in combat in World War II and some recent studies of forms of symbolic adaptation in psychotic patients with reference to some sociocultural features.

The grouping of observations from such varied sources arises from the thesis that the fear of death and the defenses against such fear cannot be considered only in terms of biologically based drives and instincts such as the drive for self-preservation. Rather the idea of death takes on form and meaning only in a social or cultural context. Under certain circumstances death is not feared but actually sought as in the altruistic type of suicide described by Durkheim.[1] We live in a culture in which there is disapproval of and shame about death, particularly from certain diseases. Only in recent years have obituaries included the fact that a person died of cancer rather than "a long illness." We either don't talk about death to children or mention it only in euphemisms. As physicians, we are not nearly so likely to say that a patient has died as to say that he has ceased, terminated, or exited. Several years ago physicians were polled by specialty as to whether patients should be told when they had cancer. The highest proportion of affirmative answers came from dermatologists and psychiatrists, probably because the former deal with many comparatively benign lesions and the latter, who see few patients with cancer, feel in principle that they should know. Probably the most difficult idea for Western man to accept is that death is a permanent condition and attempts to deny the end of existence are a central theme of much religious belief.

In patients with certain types of brain tumor and other forms of brain damage who face the threat of permanent incapacity and death, a major defense is that of denial.[2] This may take various forms. The patient may completely deny that he is ill or disabled in any way. Or he way attribute some manifestations of illness to some trivial cause such as stating that he is in the hospital for stomach trouble or that he cannot move his (paralyzed) arm because it is sore from an injection. A particularly interesting form of denial or anosognosia, literally lack of knowledge of disease, occurs in the toxic encephalopathy associated with severe burns. Here, the patient may deny not only the trauma but also the resulting disfigurement and deformity. Other patients respond to questions about illness and testing of their capacities with euphoric joking, frequently with a sexual content, mixed with paranoid complaints and delusions about food, money, and physical maltreatment.

Patients with complete denial are generally bland and euphoric with apparent disregard of their disabilities and their fatal implications. This attitude may be coupled with paranoid expressions as the patient dramatically blames some aspect of incapacity on the malice or cruelty of others. Sometimes the change from a euphoric heaven to a paranoid hell can occur in a single interview. Thus, one patient first denied having just had an arteriogram, but when pressed complained angrily that he had been stuck in the buttock with a needle. Usually patients maintain what seems to be a serene faith that they are not ill. Thus, a woman remarked, "I know my arm doesn't move, but I have the feeling that I'm not paralyzed."

Accompanying these forms of explicit and implicit denial are the phenomena of disorientation and paraphasia. In disorientation for place, the patient misnames the hospital or puts it close to his home or place of business. Paraphasia involves the selective mislabeling of objects having to do with personal problems, particularly those of the illness. Thus, patients make errors in the naming of such objects as thermometers, rubber gloves, and plastic straws while designating correctly other articles of comparable complexity and familiarity.

In many cases the disability is denied in one form of language and admitted in another. A patient who refuses to accept the fact that he has had a craniotomy may complain about the "sawing and hammering" that has been done on his head. While he misnames objects, he can generally demonstrate their use correctly. A patient who is disoriented for place persists in misrepresenting the hospital even though the name is before him in full view. While he may deny being ill in any way, he accepts medication and submits to surgical procedures without question. Such observations indicate that the manifestations of behavior cannot be directly equated with defects in memory or insight or regarded as the external representation of some discrete psychophysiological drive. The denial is not caused by the brain injury per se. Rather the milieu of brain function determines the particular level of symbolic organization or language in which the denial is expressed, whether in delusional form or as a hope or wish. All of the phenomena described occur in persons with normal brain function and it is likely that situations of extreme stress may produce, in transient fashion, conditions of brain function comparable to those following certain types of trauma. The effect of the injury is to make the symbolic patterns more condensed and enduring and to cause the individual to be more unaware that he is using language rather than designating reality itself.

Along with the symbolic patterns that have been described, there is much use of other forms of language variously classed as confabulations, metaphors, clichés, platitudes, and banal expressions. These also have an adaptive function and may appear along with delusions and disorientation or replace them in the process of recovery. After sustaining a head injury a patient may fabricate a story of how it happened. For example, soldiers who had been in automobile wrecks told stories of having been hurt in a parachute descent or of having been shot by counterintelligence agents. It became apparent that such confabulations were metaphorical or allegorical representations of current problems and disabilities. Thus, the officer who was "shot by counterintelligence agents" was referring to an intellectual deficit about which he did not otherwise express concern. Further, the particular symbol was chosen because it related the patient in his social environment and imparted a *feeling* of reality to his experience. For example, the paratrooper who confabulated about his "parachute getting all fouled up" was not only symbolizing his predicament, but also attempting to achieve a sense of identity. Subsequent interviews with these men indicated that they were otherwise rather lonely and isolated boys who had derived their main sense of esteem and belonging from membership in a special group with a special language. The confabulation thus has the negative aspect of denial and the positive one of a striving for a feeling of reality or identity by reason of the role of the symbol as an element in a pattern of social relatedness.

Clichés, banalities, and stereotyped and trite expressions are also forms of "social language."[4] Patients talk of having been hit on the head with a "blunt instrument" or having gotten a headache while "waiting for a street car." A soldier explained his being confined to a wheel chair as a "matter of policy" and his illness as a "military secret."

Similarly the language we use about death is most significant. Slang expressions such as "kicking the bucket" and euphemistic references to "meeting one's Maker" and gaining "eternal rest" seem to impart a special quality of meaning and validity by reason of the way they relate the individual in a social milieu.

The degree to which the ideas of illness and death are perceived as "real" depends on the social background, the degree of stress, and the level of brain function. Patients with marked explicit negation of illness are described as having had a need for denial even before the development of changes in brain function. They were characterized as having been conscientious, compulsive, perfectionistic people who regarded health and efficiency as personal responsibilities. Health and work were moral values. Falling ill with resulting inability to work was not simply a matter of bad fortune, but involved a sense of personal failure and a loss of status and identity. Such people, and they include many of us here today, gain a sense of identity through social relationships involving work and efficiency. When they are disabled they become socially isolated and the manifestations of illness and the prospect of death have little meaning. The greater the stress the more unawareness there is of the interaction in the socially organized environment and only those experiences that are components of a social pattern are felt as real and part of the self.

When other persons have been killed in the accident in which a patient has been injured there is frequently denial of the death. It may be verbally explicit or it may be part of amnesia. During the amnesic period the patient does not inquire as to the fate of his companions or seem interested when told. An interesting feature of the retrograde amnesia in these cases concerns the last thing that the patient remembers prior to the crash. Like a confabulation this is often a metaphorical representation of current problems and attitudes. In the case of the survivors of fatal accidents, the last memory usually has to do with sleep. Thus, the last memory is of falling asleep in the back seat of the car, going to bed the night before the trip, or as in the case of a soldier, fainting while standing in formation a few days before the accident. The acceptance of the fact of the death by the patient generally parallels the clearing of the amnesia.

Symbols of death may also serve as an adaptive mechanism.[5] Under the same conditions of altered brain function in which the syndrome of anosognosia occurs, some patients show withdrawal, inattention, and silence. In its extreme form, this appears as the syndrome of akinetic mutism. Probably the best description of this state is that the patient "acts dead." He doesn't move, speak, eat, and seems insensitive to the prick of a pin. When there is lateralized incapacity such as hemiparesis, then there may be sharply defined hemianesthesia of a "hysterical" type.

In the less severe cases, a selectivity of response is noted in which in response to questions about the illness the patient either remains silent or answers in a dysarthric, unintelligible fashion. When such patients do speak, it is usually in a depressive vein saying that they are dead, or calling the hospital a "cemetery." The behavior may be punctuated by spells of violent overactivity.

In reviewing the social background of patients with such "imitation of death" one finds that, to a great extent, interpersonal relationships were structured in symbols of death and violence. Subjects had habitually reacted to stress with withdrawal or sleep, and silence and impassivity had been a particularly eloquent mode of expression. There seemed to have been a great expectation of violence in others and an overvaluation of the effects of physical and verbal violence, so there had been an emphasis on the avoidance of gestures that could be construed as hostile. Commonly, one got the story that the patient had a violent temper which he usually controlled. In the history, attitudes toward illness included the ignoring of symptoms, silent suffering, and more overtly dramatic representations of death and disease as in obsessional fears of cancer. It is of interest that people who have sustained brain damage in suicidal attempts, as by carbon monoxide poisoning, may have prolonged periods of "coma" unexplained by the degree of brain impairment alone.

The representation of death as an adaptive process occurs also in the affective psychoses. In the past two years, I have been comparing the symbolic content of psychotic behavior in various cultural groups in the Virgin Islands. Patients from the British colony of Tortola frequently develop acute psychotic reactions lasting for several weeks characterized by stupor and overactivity with much talk of killing and death, frequently in a context of religion and the spirit world. Tortola is a rather primitive agricultural island with a population of seven thousand. There is an arbitrarily rigid system of raising children with great emphasis on obedience and respect involving much physical violence and threats and invoking of religious authority. Tortola has been called "The Holy Island." There are many superstitions, beliefs, and practices with rituals to forestall the evil spirits of people who have died. It is believed that at death one's good spirit goes to Jesus while the other remains to cause fatal diseases and harm unless properly placated. Religious teaching places great stress on punishment for sin; funerals and other church functions are the main social activities. It is a culture where a principal channel of social relatedness involves symbols of death and violence.

In combat situations symbols of death may enable the individual to remove himself from the threat of mutilation and destruction. Soldiers have remarked that in very frightening situations that look hopeless, they lose their fear when they decide they are already dead. The letters written home by Japanese kamikaze fliers[6] indicated that they regarded death by crashing into an enemy carrier as a fulfillment of life, equating it with filial piety and preservation of their country. Faith and belief seemed to be buttressed by such metaphorical language as "the blossoms fall but the tree lives" or "death shall be clean like the shattering of crystal." (Yet these same men felt the same fear when exposed to American air raids as did anyone else.) It is when the symbolic element, death, is part of a pattern which identifies one with cultural values and enables him to avoid social isolation that it ceases to be nothingness.

Thus, the concept of death may be integrated into symbolic patterns at various levels of interaction in a socially organized environment. In one context it arouses anxiety and dread while in another it serves to insulate the individual against the dangers of his physical environment. It is likely that there is a homeostatic mechanism in which the physiological and metabolic changes accompanying fear cause the type of alteration in brain function that enables a new symbolic organization to be formed and maintained as a means of adaptation to stress.

REFERENCES

1. Durkheim, E.: *Suicide.* Glencoe, Ill., The Free Press, 1951.
2. Weinstein, E. A., and Kahn, R. L.: *Denial of Illness: Symbolic and Physiological Aspects.* Springfield, Thomas, 1955.
3. Weinstein, E. A., Kahn, R. L., and Malitz, S.: Confabulation as a social process. *Psychiatry, 19:*383, 1956.

4. Weinstein, E. A.: Changes in language pattern as adaptive mechanisms. Chapter 16 in *Psychopathology of Communications*. P. H. Hoch and J. Zubin, Eds. New York, Grune and Stratton, 1958.
5. Weinstein, E. A., Kahn, R. L., and Slote, W. H.: Withdrawal, inattention, and pain asymbolia. *A.M.A. Arch. Neurol. & Psychiat.*, 74:235, 1955.
6. Inoguchi, R., Nakajima, T., with Pineau, R.: *The Divine Wind: Japan's Kamikaze Force in World War II*. Annapolis, U. S. Naval Institute, 1958.

INDEX